Bill W.

A Strange Salvation

A Biographical Novel

Also by Paul Hourihan:

Ramakrishna and Christ, The Supermystics:
   New Interpretations

The Death of Thomas Merton, A Novel
   A Confessional Portrayal of the Last Day in the
   Life of the Famous Catholic Monk and Writer

Bill W.

A Strange Salvation

A **Biographical Novel** Based on Key Moments in the Life of Bill Wilson, the Alcoholics Anonymous Founder, and a Probing of His Mysterious 11-Year Depression

PAUL HOURIHAN

Vedantic Shores Press
Redding, California

Published by: Vedantic Shores Press
                 P.O. Box 493100
                 Redding, CA 96049
                 info@vedanticshorespress.com
                 http://www.VedanticShoresPress.com

Cover design by: Emily Dawidowicz of Fleshcolour New Media http://www.fleshcolour.com

The Twelve Steps and Twelve Traditions are reprinted with permission of
Alcoholics Anonymous World Services, Inc. ("A.A.W.S.") Permission to
reprint the Twelve Steps and Twelve Traditions does not mean that
A.A.W.S. has reviewed or approved the contents of this publication, or that
AA necessarily agrees with the views expressed herein. AA is a program of
recovery from alcoholism *only*—use of the Twelve Steps and Twelve
Traditions in connection with programs and activities which are patterned
after AA, but which address other problems, or in any other non-AA
context, does not imply otherwise.

DISCLAIMER: Although a work of fiction, this story is based in part on
true events. Certain liberties have been taken with names and dates, and
some characters have been invented, as well as most of the dialogue.

Cataloguing Data:

Hourihan, Paul
        Bill W., A Strange Salvation : a biographical novel based on key
    moments in the life of Bill Wilson, the Alcoholics Anonymous founder, and
    a probing of his mysterious 11-year depression / Paul Hourihan. -1st ed.
        Includes bibliographical references.
        ISBN 1-931816-02-6   Softcover
        1. W., Bill— Fiction. 2. Alcoholics—Biography—Fiction.
    3. Alcoholics Anonymous— Fiction.
        LCCN 2002115556

Sobriety and the discovery that a sober life is possible is the truth for alcoholics, but beyond sobriety there are other truths available to the seeking minds of the more thoughtful and meditative of the AA fellowship ... as well as non-alcoholics of similar potential.

This book is dedicated to them.

Acknowledgments

Our thanks to those individuals who provided information during the preliminary research period in the early 1990s including: Paul Cyr, Curator of the Special Collections Department of the New Bedford Free Public Library, and staff in New Bedford, Massachussetts; Jeannie Pickard, and staff of the Kootenay Lake Archives in Kaslo, British Columbia; and Ozzie Lepper, Proprietor of the Wilson House, Bill Wilson's birthplace in East Dorset, Vermont, for generously spending time answering questions and giving a tour of the Wilson House.

Thanks also to: Peter Wright for his peer reading and useful comments; Nula Barrett for her capable copyediting services; Emily Dawidowicz for her creative cover design; and Ralph Giovinazzo for his artistic guidance and support throughout the production phase.

Author's Note

From 1944 to 1955 Bill Wilson suffered a profound and mysterious depression which, when it has been considered at all, has never been satisfactorily accounted for. To explain, or at least understand the causes of this malaise is the purpose of the present volume.

Since the facts of his history as we know them have thrown so little light on the problem, I have not felt bound by a purely biographical or literal approach to his life to find the answer, if such be forthcoming. At the same time *Bill W., A Strange Salvation* is not entirely a novel either, but rather a creative work *based* on some of the facts of Wilson's life, while employing traditional techniques of imagination leavened and focused by the potency of meditative insight brought to bear upon all phases of the subject. Many of the scenes and mental struggles he is shown going through did not happen as far as we know—but they may have. Their inclusion is justified if, to the reader, they convince and illuminate.

Contents

Chronology

1939   *Alcoholics Anonymous,* the "Big Book," is published.

1939   September, *Liberty* article on AA published.

1941   March 1, *The Saturday Evening Post* prints an article on AA by Jack Alexander.

1943–44   Bill and Lois' first trip across the country visiting AA groups.
Winter, Bill meets the California mystics, Aldous Huxley, Christopher Isherwood and Gerald Heard.

1944   The beginning of Bill's depression.

1950   July, The Twelve Traditions are accepted at the First International AA Convention.
November, Dr. Bob dies.

1951   The First General Service Conference meets.

1953   *Twelve Steps and Twelve Traditions* is published.

1955   July, at the St. Louis Convention, Bill gives AA its formal release into maturity.
Bill's depression ends.

1971   January 24, Bill dies.

"Thank you for your lives."

—Bill Wilson's last words to Alcoholics Anonymous.

In the midst of the darkness rose the thought like an indictment that the ovations from which he had fled were a goad to live up to the faith and hero worship that had inspired them. Standing in the center of their accolades, was he to have reached higher into the spiritual dimensions of his unknown self and become the reborn man their homage invited?

The thought pursued him into the depths of silent hours and only gradually, with spasms of guilt and an unaccountable fear, did he succeed in putting it to rest.

A recurrent sense of futility about this latest venture, as of so many before, had clung to him as he drove the twenty miles to Twin Rivers. He would go through with it but the intuition of impending failure was strong. And the irony of his objective had struck him again, as it had Lois: he of all people appearing incognito, seeking invisibility.

But he had to keep trying. What else was there to do?

Twin Rivers was a new group. There if anywhere he might recover the blessedness of anonymity, cease for an hour to be himself.

The meeting would begin at 8:30 p.m. He had timed his arrival for five minutes later, had pulled over to the side of the parking area, and now waited until the last car had emptied. In another minute he would quickly get out, slip into the meeting-hall, and unobtrusively find a seat at the back. As he waited, a mood of tension had taken possession of him. He felt like a lawbreaker.

Then—it happened. Just as he was about to leave his car he spotted a tall, lanky, gray-haired individual getting out of his own vehicle some fifty feet away, a recovered alcoholic he had known for ten years, certain to recognize him.

There was no way he could escape notice. Larry, an outgoing gregarious type, would infallibly draw the group's attention to him, the chairman of the meeting would then request him to "honor them with his words of wisdom," the applause of everyone in the room would compel him to oblige them, and the whole purpose of his being there would be lost.

Chagrined, he started up the car and headed back to Bedford Hills. It was months since the last of these experiments had been successful. Shouldn't he give them up once and for all? Or try again one more time?

The tension had vanished, replaced by the familiar cluster of weakness, spiritual depletion, emptiness. His daily companions.

But also—relief: he wouldn't have to go now.

Prologue

God knows, he had tried everything.

Perhaps talked about it a little too freely, thinking to lighten the burden. But it wouldn't be reduced, would not be trivialized.

It clung like a living adversary to his nerves, to every part of him day after day, month after month, year after year. Five years now. *Longer*....

Whole days in bed in strange immobility, fears and anxieties to match anything he had known during the thirties, the debility, almost the nonexistence of will.

How did it begin, how did he get this way? It was like death, with the added burden of feeling guilty about it—responsible for the whole thing.

Long before, he had seen that the drinking was a disguised hunger for God, just as AA itself was another form of God-searching. But how did this silent hell relate to all that?

His punishment for not having set out for God, once he had perceived, and clearly understood, why he had drunk so obsessively?

Not a punishment from God—rather, his own?

I am mine own executioner.

And in no way worse than the fateful effect on his psyche of all that *wrong thinking, deluded emotion* over the five long years ... *changing* him, making it ever more difficult to implement the insights which for brief periods seemed to give him hope he might liberate himself. It was the *will* that was undermined by the false thinking, the will he needed to make himself act.

He could not seem to *want* to act.

He had what passed for understanding—people had admired his writing, his clear thinking, and his spiritual guidance in the AA literature. But the understanding had been only on one level. He had habitually lived on the surface of his mind except for that single moment at Towns fifteen years before. Invited, *importuned* to go deeper, to discover who he was and perhaps what the deity was, he had reneged, failed to embrace the new challenge.

Adding *guilt* to the rest of the misery, consuming himself with perceptions that may have been true, and a way out, but lacking power to enact them—usually even to remember them, and hence what light they had had redounded against him, turning the depression into despair.

In the armchair facing the windows and the fading light of afternoon, he stirred with an ache of nostalgia, remembering that day in Towns at the end of 1934, when in a moment a light of revelation, sudden and profound, had lifted him out of the fear of alcoholism and the craving to drink—that sacred moment of his life which every year he privately observed, out of which had grown the whole AA movement.

What had happened to that moment on the mountain?

He had failed to renew it, to seek its successors, to remold his personality in accordance with its promptings, had failed to make it the continuing center of his life—which the once-a-year remembrance did not begin to do!

More, he had denigrated the divine contact by the way he had referred to it in AA circles, and elsewhere—invariably as his *hot flash*. To accommodate himself to the spiritual level of other AA members had been his self-proclaimed motive, for he had gradually realized that what had happened to him was not going to happen to others, saving the rare exception like Chris Eastman. Dr. Bob had hardly understood what he was talking about.

Nevertheless, whatever his motives in such demeaning references, the blinding insight into the actuality of the divine presence had become a mere hot flash. The most exalted moment of his life he had transformed into a democratic colloquialism.

He had made *them* comfortable, reassured that his mysterious experience, known throughout AA, was just a little elevation of spirit such as might come to any of them at any time. But what had *he* made of the moment? And of his own mind's relation to it? What had he done to his fine-tuned approach to the deity during periods of prayer? Could he then pray with an appropriate reverence, ease, self-respect?

I have served mankind all too well, he thought.

He remembered a line from Shakespeare. *Had I but served my God with half the zeal I served my king, he would not in mine age have left me naked to my enemies.*

Change *king* to *fellows*, and the comparison was accurate.

He paused, uncomfortable with his thought.

Had the Lord truly turned away? For these five years it often seemed that he had. But that could not *really* be. The Lord's grace, Gerald Heard had reminded him earlier this year, was always blowing, always available. It was *he* who had turned away, not the Lord.

It was his *ego* that had turned away. (*His self-will run riot,* as he had written recently.) And turned *him* away with it. It was the diabolical ego, wanton, tireless, cunning—back again, newly entrenched, aggressive, ferocious, using the depression and *taking its form*—that was behind it all, just as it was ego behind his drinking and his alcoholic mentality in earlier years.

In frustrate rage it had strangled him again, determined this time to win a total victory and let him alone only when there was little left of significance in him for the enemy to be troubled about!

Yes—that is what it seemed to be ... *the depression was his ego attacking him at the deepest level.* No wonder he was having trouble understanding it. For who—standing outside its perimeter, cut off from the experience, good souls like Lois herself, for one—could really believe that? He thought an AA member could, but he was loath to frighten them unnecessarily with such tidings when in maintaining their sobriety they had problems enough.

He stirred with the realization that despite the dead end into which he had been led—the morass in which he floundered, the lack of energy, and the distortion of all his values—there remained some sense, sufficiently sharp, of right and wrong, of real and unreal.

In the end he knew it was the spiritual alone that would provide him with the answers he needed.

Just as it had been the spiritual *by default* that had generated the causes.

Causes....

Magic word.

The *real* cause still eluded him, but he *felt* what the truth was, or where it was leading him. And the question of his hypocrisy, his false-facing, his backsliding, his failure to *level* with the spiritual side of his nature, was central to it.

His lack of any real faith....

Here he was, at fifty-three, with no genuine grasp of religion or faith in God ... and *therefore,* perhaps, this depression?

Mirror of his emptiness of faith.

For if he *did* have faith, would it not have guided him to find a way out of the dilemma, and never to have had it—on this scale, at least—in the first place?

The irony that he should be giving spiritual counsel to tens of thousands, and unable to follow his own prescriptions!

What he was going through was in its way as bad as the alcoholism, with less of a respite from the burden. At least when he had drunk there had been periods of planning and enthusiasm, various desperate projects of hope, all illusory, to be sure, but better than this blanket of leaden apathy over his mind, that had *become* his mind.

Even the things he did that were outwardly positive were vitiated by the knowledge that they were but half measures, temporary and surface diversions from the main business of his life.

Which was to look at the wall.

Yes, diversions—exhibitions of an effete, almost nonexistent strength of mind—to prove something to himself and to those, far too many, he suspected who were watching, that he was on a comeback, would soon be returning to himself.

When he spoke unavoidably at the meetings, went to the office downtown to dictate to Nell the long overdue correspondence, met with the oft-disappointed member of the fellowship, consulted with the therapists or the clergy (*three* now), joined Lois for meals or sessions of music appreciation in the living room of Stepping Stones, or took his solitary walks in the woods out of sight of everybody, there was the hovering reminder that he could soon return to the studio, to his armchair or the cot, and the wall.

Every day more and more looking forward to his times of retreat, the warm isolating seductive warmth of his surrenders, the sexual-like enveloping in the lethal cocoon.

What had *really* caused it? *Five and a half years,* with no hint that the end was in sight. What could remove it? Or who could?

It was fully the equal of his alcoholism.

In those surreal years that ended at Towns, it was the return to drinking and its all-consoling prospect that steadied him during times of fugitive constructive behavior ... the counterpart to his present abandonments to the black power.

He had thought of suicide and the other suicide—drinking again—many times, but terror inhibited him, the desolation at the thought of what its effect would be on numberless lives.

There ... the seed of the whole depression.

Admittedly his periodic compulsive exhibitions of self-respect—the twice-weekly trip to the office for a few dazed hours each time, the AA talks he absolutely could not escape (like the one in the Manhattan Central church auditorium tomorrow night), writing letters when he had to ... all of this *forced* him to keep the danger within *some* bounds, kept him from an even worse condition.

So he was grateful for those things ... but, again, even more grateful when they were over and he was free to return to the silent agony.

Yet never giving in entirely, even as he seemed to yield. Still trying everything—and letting it be known that he was.

• • •

With the rough, jocular humor of AA, often enough directed *lèse majesté* at its founder, he had been advised more than once to "Work the Twelve Steps, Bill. Get back on the program!"—return to the straight and narrow path he had chalked out for alcoholics.

But you needed *will* for that, a will depression had sapped. He had will only for outer things. The safer things.

Besides, he didn't have to work the steps—he had written them!

Like St. Paul. After showing others the way to safety, he asked: "Shall I myself become a castaway?"

He thought of Reverend Sam and Father Ed.

Sam Shoemaker, the Episcopal minister based in Manhattan, and Father Ed Dowling, the Irish Jesuit who came all the way from St. Louis that night nine years ago to meet him. Both early and persistent friends of AA. Both thoroughly aware of what he was going through and each deeply solicitous not only for his sake but for the sake of AA. Already there were rumors that his frequent absences had been caused by his return to drinking and his shame about showing his face in AA circles.

They would pray for him and had been doing so for the five years—thus far to no effect whatever.

But Lois too and countless others in AA had been praying for him—all of them together lofting a vast army of fervent prayers to pressure the divine throne to please see to it that Bill Wilson of Bedford Hills, New York, was released from the black dog of a depression that had been killing him since the beginning of 1944.

Perhaps if he could generate the *will* to throw off even the beginnings of this apathy, more good would be accomplished than through all their prayers.

God helps those who help themselves. Even the prayers of saints could not help a man who could not—*would* not—help himself.

Was that true—*would* not?

So Sam and Father Ed were faithfully praying for him, and their prayers, he was to believe, were somehow more to be listened to by the supreme than the less holy prayers of mere laity. True, they did not say or act or imply that. But when a clergyman left you, saying "I'll pray for you," that was the impression they left. The look on their faces was eloquent with that presumption.

Which did not mean he did not cherish their advice, normally so practical and earnest, well-intended, and behind it their image of him as representative of the entire AA movement.

Yes, he appreciated what they said, even if both sounded professionally similar in what they recommended, as though under one or another set of circumstances they would automatically respond to the person in difficulty in a prescribed manner.

In this case their counsel was that his five years' misery was God's way of testing him. See it as a blessing in disguise, Bill. God's heroes are always tested. Hammered steel is passed through many fires before it is selected for the most extreme pressures.

But he didn't believe this. Rather than pointing to some unknown glorious future, more likely the depression had to do with his past, with what had *already* happened to him. Through the pathways of memory, the labyrinths of time, the roads already taken, the answer might be found ... though he knew not how to go about discovering it.

As for being tested by God, there was another reason why he felt that was not true in his case: he had made no real commitment to the higher power. His most effective prayers on the two memorable occasions of his life—at Towns in December 1934 and in the Akron Mayflower hotel five months later when it all began—were not prayers of commitment but prayers for release and deliverance, prayers to be freed from the desire to stop drinking or not to start drinking again.

Since then?

His life was being carried forward on the momentum of what he had done in those early years. Now the momentum had wound down like a clock.

No, no renewal. No personal relationship with the deity. No grace to keep him from the dark destroyer who came on such seductive approaches.

That is why the clerics' talk about being tested rang so hollow.

Was his depression a *punishment* for failure to make a commitment? No, rather it was itself the emptiness that marked an absence of committed will—and his refusal to make a commitment, allowing himself to be swayed into *not* doing so, was an example of raw ego in action.

He should know. Few could equal an alcoholic in nurturing monster-egos, and he was the foremost alcoholic of all.

His weekly visits to Fulton Sheen was more of the same—pure vanity. For the monsignor only took top figures for his Catholic proselytizing, although what he was supposed to be doing was to "explain" Catholicism. And it was ego-comforting to know that others knew of his mysterious consultations. Admittedly there was a fascination with Catholicism—its age and atmosphere, its certainty in areas where he himself was full of uncertainties, its offer of an ancient maternal bosom to soothe the heart's cry, therefore, it seemed, its truth *also.*

But the whole thing was impossible for him. The Roman church was simply too authoritarian for someone with his fierce individualism, his ever-questioning mind ... too self-righteous, unable to examine its own sins, of which there were so many in its history. Also, if he converted, the effect on the non-Catholic membership would be harshly negative, to say the least.

Then there was the quote from a newspaper summarizing a talk Sheen had given recently. The prelate had called alcoholism a moral disease: patently a *disease* on the physical level, and *moral* because of weakness of will and utter irresponsibility. Hence, *moral disease*— disturbing sound. With that approach Msgr. Sheen could have helped no alcoholic to stop drinking—as indeed had been the sorry record of religion in its handling of alcoholism. How much better AA's "a physical allergy coupled with a mental obsession."

So why was he still going? His vanity still liked the idea of one big man meeting with another, Bill Wilson and Fulton Sheen, the famed Catholic orator. Each *sui generis.* And it was something to do on Saturdays, another place to go.

Another few hours of activity that took him away from himself and the staring eye of conscience.

• • •

It wasn't any better with the psychiatrists, first with Harry Tiebout and now with his successor closer at hand, Frances Weekes. A psychological explanation of *causes* was ultimately of no real effect, because those causes were true only on one level of his personality, had little or no relevance on profounder levels: He was guilty over AA's success, the argument went. His sense of unworthiness, stemming from childhood conflicts and deprivations, made him unready for AA's ascending achievement. His depression was a judgment passed on himself.

All this was valid enough, but only a metaphysical insight, such as he felt himself stumbling towards, could go deep enough to really satisfy. For a recovered alcoholic, having gone through the hell of personality and its extremes was nothing if not a metaphysical animal. What Harry had said in his analysis was reasonable—but fairly obvious. He didn't have to drive the sixty miles to Blythewood to hear *that*.

Harry, valuable AA friend though he had always been, tended to fix on the immaturity of alcoholics anyway—a continuing weakness in his therapy.

The psychological explanation couldn't and didn't relieve him. It remained an *exercise* for Harry Tiebout, probably answering his own questions about the problem, but not Bill Wilson's. Reflecting a mind— the scientific mind, as such, concerned with laws rather than people— more interested in alcoholism than in the alcoholic, the depression rather than the sufferer.

The newest psychiatrist, was trying to persuade him that his total sacrifice for AA had stunted his personality—hence the depression: he had failed to provide his life with enough satisfaction apart from making himself so constantly available to AA demands.

A conventional, materialistic analysis. Dr. Weekes, otherwise personable and kind, overlooked the fact that when he had been most dedicated to the claims of AA on his time and life he had been happier than he had ever been. Sacrifice in a cause as great as AA brought about a satisfaction which no amount of "individual" development could match. Even now he could not deny that.

So, her advice had made him feel good for just a short time. It was a transparent counsel of self-serving that reflected typical psychiatric philosophy.

• • •

Then Lois, his wife of thirty-one years ... who had gone so far as to admit, in a moment of great impatience and confusion at her husband's plight, that she was "not sympathetic—didn't know *how* to be so." A simplistic, black-and-white woman, his Lois, stalwart ally of so many battles in a shared past. Without her he would have been dead, AA unborn. Hence the tremendous general debt owed her.

But her grand days were past. He loved her, felt gratitude and admiration, but her lack of growth was self-evident, a reflection of his. If *he* had grown, as he had been doing through the end of 1943, she would have also, to match him ... or else faded away.

If Lois was a mirror to her husband's state, then that state was not promising!

No wonder she was humiliated at his predicament. His condition of withdrawal, suicidal in its scope, was a public affront to *her,* an aspersion on her womanly, wifely role.

Heroic, exemplary in the twenties and thirties when he had drunk maniacally, the best she could offer now was: "Why can't you pull yourself together and be a man again?"

The strain between them had grown too uncomfortable to bear much longer. For both. An AA member skilled in carpentry and masonry offered to do the work building the studio for him. The reason given was that he needed more privacy for his writing.

Which was completely accepted by one and all. Lois was an icon in the movement. No one could have guessed the truth.

So this retreat was the compromise solution, which she tolerated in silent mortification. At least this way she didn't have to see quite as much of him when he was *like that*, for when he joined her for activities in common, beginning with meals, he struggled to show normal signs of responsiveness ... as he remembered them.

He seemed to understand her quite well, and did not resent—at least most of the time—her impatience. After all, she feared he would return to drinking, which would have brought down in ruins the wondrous new world they had known for fifteen years past, a world in which she occupied a very special and honored place in the esteem of many. Her impatience was an aspect of her fear that he would destroy everything they had built up.

Even in the darkest depths he knew—beyond any shadow of doubt—that he *could* not drink, that he would be physically, perhaps mortally prevented from drinking by the power that had rescued him and all of AA from slavery.

She did not know that. Did not know that he was the only man in the world who would not be allowed to drink alcohol ever again. (The dying Dr. Bob was no longer in question.)

She feared, wondered, prayed, as others did. But he *knew*.

That was the unlifted shadow that lay over him. The knowledge, communicated directly from the divine.

It was no longer a matter of desiring a certain goal of permanent sobriety and of attaining it. He was in fact *sentenced* to that ideal, made to adhere to it, his own choice having nothing to do with it.

Besides the burden of his personality struggles to cope with, he had *that* to carry as well.

He was the least free man in the country.

He stirred in the armchair, his gaze vacantly directed through the large windows upon the first autumn foliage beginning to appear in the trees surrounding the studio and across much of the one and a half acres of their property.

Well, he had not married her for her wisdom but for her simple strength of character, her steadiness, stamina, and her prudent good sense—all the things he needed in a woman, known when he was twenty. It had not been, strictly speaking, a love relationship for him, but in the long run it may have served him better. Someone with his emotionality (despite that rugged, masculine exterior) and capacity for extreme undertakings, his impulsive reaching-out to life's farther possibilities, his heavy-handed egoism—needed someone with traits and resources such as Lois possessed.

Hence he had never regretted their marriage, had always felt fortunate he had found her when he did, very early in the game, blessed that she had been able to outlast his alcoholism, holding to her role through the heartbreak and devastation of a decade.

No, he didn't resent her. Who was he, creature of shadows, half-dead man, to resent anybody?

Least of all a wife who had tried, really tried, to do her best over the whole of their married life. Perhaps because his feeling for her was more one of affection and deepest appreciation he was able to put up with *her* shortcomings ... since he had not expected the utmost from her. As a result, what he had gotten over the years was a level of cooperation and usefulness surpassing his expectations.

Besides, women gave men so much more than they received that normally a man had no right to complain about anything in marriage. He had only to envisage how his own life would have been without Lois, depending on himself, living a bachelor existence, and he had his answer. So he was grateful, and able to feel that way without undue effort.

Was it possible that—like so much in his life—he had been *led* to marry someone with whom the unique love-mood would be absent, feeling always—over and above the spirit of gratefulness for her—that lack, something missing from his experience, though fully capable of it, never having known the love the heart dreams of—except that time long ago, in Manchester?

Had he been robbed by destiny of a great, abiding love to equip him for a special task, manipulated in order to throw his emotions towards another ideal, that of humanity—to be served in the absence of more absorbing passions?

So it had turned out, surpassing his dreams to be of service to the world. During his nine years of glory, from the end of 1934 to the end of 1943, he had done more than he would have thought possible, begetting a movement of such magnitude that it had called forth another, seemingly of equal proportion—this incessant treacherous fog over his mind that had *become* his mind and the very tissue of his thinking.

But the record was clear, what he had done was still an incomprehensible miracle: first overcoming addiction in himself and then in a hundred thousand others, soon—probably in his lifetime—to be a million. Found a key to open any door, a solution to any tragedy of the soul, for alcoholism was a *constellation* of illnesses and mysteries, and the AA way—embodied in the Twelve Steps—was applicable anywhere, and was already being found to be.

So, in the midst of the gloom and debility of will ... some satisfaction.

Yes ... early deprived ... *set up* ... to bring about the great thing that had been done. To bring about the alcoholism itself, which in its time was a kind of religious ecstasy, *a mysticism of craving,* whereby he fed his soul on dreams of greatness to come, though it never came as he had dreamed, but as it had to.

The strangeness of it—that one should apprehend so much about one's condition, grasp so many subtleties, probe so familiarly into hidden corners of the psyche, and yet know so little about what really went on within, or why, to help explain what and who one was, and how one had gotten into the Slough of Despond that presently characterized one's way of life!

But still trying everything.

On days when he managed to get out of bed, his daily walk along the wooded paths adjacent to his property, each time a struggle to begin, but each time—or almost so—succeeding. *That* much he could do. Then the challenge of lasting the quarter mile, then a little longer, sometimes the half mile, even the mile, then sometimes—with rests along the way—a mile and a half, trying as he plod along to synchro-nize his in-and-out respiration with his pacing. Afterwards feeling better, uplifted, briefly pulled out of his condition, but as yet unable to find a way to take advantage of his exhilaration.

And the osteopathic adjustments ... solving a psychological impasse by manipulating misplaced vertebrae. Even hormone treatments ... which admittedly, like the osteopathy, had done some good. Everything probably helped. But so long as he failed to come to grips with the central problem, which he well knew, he would never shake off this thralldom, no matter how many individual good things he resorted to.

Deep within he knew—*felt,* rather—for he seemed to be led forward through the forest of his mind by the light of emotions, that the answer lay in a direction he had not taken, on a path still unknown.

A path he could almost name but from which he resolutely turned away.

The greatest irony of all was that he was not able to benefit from attendance at AA gatherings—an advantage every member in the fellowship had over him. As he had discovered once again at Twin Rivers last night, he could not quietly drive to some unfamiliar group, slip into a back seat and soak his mind anonymously in the life-generating atmosphere of the meetings. He was always recognized and pressured into speaking.

What he least wished to do for the last five years—speak at AA!

Its father and architect—in flight from the movement he had fostered!

Abruptly he got up from the armchair, stretched, lit a cigarette. Tomorrow night he would be on display again, having promised the Manhattan Central group weeks ago he would help them with their fifth anniversary meeting. Two of its members were comrades from the early days and he could not disappoint them.

Tomorrow. Would that be the night they found him out? Sooner or later it had to happen. The only question was—when? Meanwhile he could give them the well-rehearsed story of his own career, of which, despite the endless repetitions, they never tired.

And that heavy, demanding, slurring, growling, New England twanging, self-important voice with its monotonous timbre! He well knew how he sounded. A tape recording someone had made of one of his recent talks had, when he had heard it, only depressed him further.

The *heaviness* in particular had affected him—of alcoholics generally. As he listened to the recording he had felt the quality of his own—almost unchanged from 1934. The same with practically all of them. Dr. Bob particularly—his personality unchanged from the day he had met him, still gripped daily with the desire to drink—a heroic ordeal for poor Bob. He had told him that he counted the days of his sobriety like a prisoner counting the days until his parole.

Yes, that heaviness in them. In himself, their role model par excellence, perhaps more than any.

The heaviness was the *ego*—always that!—in its grosser manifestation. Do things my way, I know best. If you listen to me everything will prosper.... Indeed, taking that stand without realizing one had done so, fatuously self-complacent, invulnerably opaque.

Even when sober, alcoholics projected that insatiable quality, unaware of it for the most part. The element nonalcoholics must have found keenly difficult to bear. And, withal, the dense self-approval!

Only Chris Eastman had seemed free of the phenomenon: doubtless the main source of his attraction for him.

He inhaled disconsolately on the cigarette.

While on his feet, he looked into the small mirror on the bookshelf behind his desk, unhappy with what he saw: the fraudulence still undiscovered, the signs of age, the slackness, the somber mask of self-obsession, the self-cozening satisfaction *stamped* on the features, the obtuseness, the eyes without luster, the flesh without tone, the twisted strained grin beneath the morose discontent.

Was this the man who had powered AA into being?

No, the man who had done that was hidden, buried deep within him, under the sloth and enervation of these five years. If he could find that man again, he would throw off the burden and be himself once more.

He turned away and thought for a moment. He recalled a photograph taken of him and Dr. Bob sometime around 1940 in Bob's Akron living-room, the two seated on armchairs pulled together. The picture had evoked a completely different impression. Dr. Bob came across as he always had—expressionless, granitic in his self-satisfaction, alcoholically *set in his ways*. He himself had radiated a lighter, more buoyant, almost spiritual quality—the heavy-handedness, the self-engrossment muted.

The contrast struck him between that photograph of himself and almost all the others he recalled, including the image that just now had looked back at him in the mirror. He wondered what the answer was. He lingered a moment or two longer on the challenge, sensing some plausible significance there.

The picture had been taken sometime towards the end of the early struggle, before Jack Alexander's 1941 *Post* article had been felt. In other words, before victory had been grasped: while it was still vital that AA be nursed and protected in every possible way—which was why he had made trip after trip to Akron during that era.

Fundamental to AA's thriving was first of all unbroken sobriety for him and Dr. Bob, for if either drank again—especially if he, the prime mover, did so—the foundations of the movement would be shattered and its future almost certainly destroyed.

But Bob's powers of self-control, though in fact he had remained continuously without alcohol since June of 1935, had always left him uneasy. His frank acknowledgment that the desire to drink was a daily experience was matched by the same uninhibited, heedless, devil-may-care attitudes that must have characterized his behavior during his active alcoholism.

There was also his emotional relationship with himself as his AA *sponsor,* the one who had rescued him from his alcoholic hopelessness. If the two of them remained at cross-purposes very long, it might provide Bob with the last straw he needed to help him reach for the bottle, while blaming Bill Wilson for his lapse.

Therefore peace and mutual agreement—visible and actual—was mandatory, not only for Dr. Bob himself, but for the members who had to see and to know there was a strong bond between the two leaders, temperamentally so unlike. That was absolutely essential quite as much as their continued sobriety, and he had exerted all his powers and summoned up all his prudence and tact to insure that it was sustained year after year.

Invariably he had deferred to Bob in their discussions, touted him from the beginning as a cofounder even though Bob himself always declined the honor, and did everything necessary to pacify Bob's alcoholic assertiveness.

"It wasn't natural for Bill," Lois, astonished, had explained to their closer friends. "He *forced* himself to do it."

And in doing what was unnatural he had almost achieved a unique breakthrough into hidden recesses of his personality. Unfortunately, back in New York the familiar power urges had possessed him as easily as ever.

In this strategic yielding to Bob he had tapped another dimension of his personality—selflessness, spirituality—and it was this element, experienced most frequently during his Akron trips, that had shone out so markedly in the photograph ... especially because while it was being snapped he had been thoroughly conscious of both Dr. Bob's strong, phlegmatic presence and of his own need of smiling self-effacement, which the photograph had well captured.

Especially could he feel that way—and obviously *look* that way— during the earlier struggling years. While there was still uncertainty about the life and death of AA—through the end of 1940—still the joy of the engagement, the flame of the new creation burning in his soul every moment, and all the overcoming of obstacles, of which there were so many, he had exuded that radiant impression. With the coming of undoubted success and victory, beginning in the spring of 1941 after the Alexander piece, he had been thrown back into alcoholic negativity. The light went from his eyes, his New England twang— never too inspiring in the best of times—began to labor with its burden of monotony. And dullness, unhappiness, depression had dominated.

Alcoholics, it seemed, could not stand success. After the unexpected triumphs in the West in the winter of 1943-1944, furnishing new and emotionally overwhelming evidence of the sweeping spread of the movement, at that precise moment the depression reared up its unreality and he began his day-to-day humiliation.

Victim of this silent terror for which there was no name, no cure.

He had not been able to endure the grand vindication of his life's work. Had felt guilty, unworthy, unfit for such honors.

That was the diagnosis. Which seemed true enough as far as it went. But the truth it contained must have been severely limited, for even the acceptance of it had been unable in the slightest to release him from the oppression and the lassitude. Real truth should liberate, recharge, renew!

He had to keep looking for another truth.

He paused, standing, in the middle of the carpeted studio room, smoking quietly, gazing out the windows onto the peaceful wooded scene of fading summer light. Lois would be gone through the dinner hour. She was organizing a new family group in New York, had left a meal for him to prepare.

First, he would diagnose himself.

The past—that was what might hold the key. On his own, without psychiatric prompting, he would retrace the major steps he had taken to bring him to where he now was.

A peculiar, comforting emotion rose up in him, and he allowed it to ride smoothly through the terrain of his mind.

He would turn again to the lights and shadows of the past, the kingdom of mystery and forgotten realizations, truths perished in the on-streaming flux. But perhaps not altogether lost. He would trace the landmark moments of his life and try to penetrate them—the epiphanies, the crises—for their meaning and truth.

The early years, the vanished summers, the hours that changed everything, the day he became an alcoholic!

The first time he had felt life moving in upon his vulnerability like the waves of the sea, *priming* him for inevitabilities, for what had to follow, *had* to come into being.

Was that true?

He thought it was. For years he had felt it as a secret truth.

If so, then nothing was to be regretted, nothing would have been better happening in any other way than it had to.

How many times, drinking, had he known this hunger for the past!

The sacred legacy. What *had* been. All that life, that passion. The future was unknown, but the past equally so. We had apparently lived it, moving as a shadow *among* shadows, everything intangible and dreamlike, but the answers lay there in the obscurity, like strange cloud formations.

We *were* our past. In exploring it one explored one's present psyche. Indeed in studying and mastering the past you understood, perhaps could predict, the future. Both meeting at the same dynamic point of present consciousness.

Where he stood now.

PART ONE

1 The Rupture

He never regretted his place of birth in the valley hamlet of East Dorset, folded closely in the Green Mountains of southern Vermont, a womb of a village where life like a fable—among dwellings shaded by sugar maples and bounded by blue-veined marble sidewalks fashioned from the nearby quarries—could magically flower.

But there were signs of other realities at work. They spoke to him a cryptic legend: that everything was interconnected.

In the Wilson house, a popular inn at the center of the village, operated by his grandmother, the widow Wilson, he had been born—in a room next to the bar.

Did that mean that drinking was to play a role in his life? Strange, for he had been warned about it, reminded that alcohol had caused trouble on his father's side of the family.

It almost seemed that even from the first hours he was being watched.

Then, his birth. His mother had suffered terribly, her protracted cries on that wintry late November night in 1895 alarming to hear. She never forgot that night. Upon delivery, she found him almost dead.

Some power, expressed through his mother's agony, did not want him in the world? The idea frightened—and thrilled him at the same time. Or *she* did not want him? This, too, frightened and dismayed but, in a way he could not fathom, intrigued him.

Was his life meant to be something special?

Mark Whalon thought so.

Ten years older than himself, one of the few in the Dorset villages with a college background, and a stubbornly independent thinker, Mark never forgot that night, and always referred to it over the years in the same tone of wonder and conviction:

"—A bitter stormy night—not one to be born in! And what with your mother's cries, which went on and on and really frightened me, I couldn't help but feel that something odd was going on. Even though I was only ten I thought that whoever was getting born in that room wasn't going to live a life like other folks but had some kind of *destiny* to fulfill—someone who was to hold high office or become a prophet or a great leader of some kind, and it was as if I was being commissioned to keep it in remembrance, never to forget it, perhaps to kind of watch over you. I thought of tales of ancient times, when heroes were born and Nature was *convulsed*. It was like that—"

And Mark had half-grinned, grimacing in an exaggerated way, all the time looking at him with a peculiar, fixed expression.

Was Mark right? He *did* feel even in those early days that he was meant to do something special in the world—but what, exactly? Mostly the feeling was like a great store of hidden energy or power that rose up to consciousness from deep within him, making him feel strange to himself and at the same time almost invincible.

How *strong* his feelings were, how *sensitive* he was to everything!

He believed he had lived before and would again; did not yet know why, but knew he would find out some day. Meanwhile the conviction, never talked about, hovered over him like a presence.

East Dorset, cradled among the mountains, was like a stage in a theater, where a new life-drama was taking place and where the playwright mysteriously left signs of his intentions.

Life itself was the mystery and he accepted early the challenge to find out what it was, why we were here, why things were the way they were—and why he was the way he was, *different* from most of the people around him.

His emotional nature, to begin with: composed of extremes, strung with wires that could convey the slightest nuance from the most turbulent to the most sensitive. Often he was carried away in its powerful oscillations.

His capacity to *feel* was his central rhythm. Life itself *was* feeling. Without it you didn't really live. Everything moved him. But he had to find out how to control his responsiveness, the better to learn the secret, find the undiscovered chord playing unheard behind the scenes. He was sure it was through feeling he would find it.

Or lose it?

Sooner or later he had to find a way to *handle* his emotions.

Until then, hoping it would be only warm and comfortable emotions that filled him, he remained aglow with feeling, like a bee on a flower, burning like a firefly in the night-fields.

Even as he made himself endearing to everyone in the two-room country school and to his neighbors, and adapted to whatever the rules were ... standing apart from others through *an excess of soul*, through his acute *feeling* nature—which he knew early he must protect from the world.

And from himself.

It was common knowledge that his parents' families had been acquaintances in East Dorset or neighboring villages for the better part of the nineteenth century. When his mother and father came of age, having known each other all their lives, they were expected to marry, partly because there were so few prospects available.

He saw elements of himself in each. Emily, a schoolteacher until marriage, was disciplined, hard-working, intellectual, devoted to education; while Gilman, manager of one of the Dorset quarries, was a simple, easy-going, humane man with a tendency to heavy drinking. He knew his mother felt superior to him.

Gradually he discovered that people with his mother's temperament always believed themselves superior to others, especially those of his father's emotional type.

His father drank too much but was a good man. Often he would sing with the family while his mother accompanied him on the melodeon: "In the Shade of the Old Apple Tree," "Wait Till the Sun Shines, Nellie," "On the Banks of the Wabash." ... Those were times he would not forget. And they would play ball together in the evening, the two of them. He would call him Christy, like the great pitcher Mathewson: "Put it there, Christy! Three strikes and he's out!" That was after he returned from the Dorset Quarry. Working in the dust and stone hour after hour must have damaged him, so that when the day was over he would crave a cool glass of ale to make him fit again for his family. Wouldn't anyone?

Did he think the same way as his mother? He was sure he did not. His father—to whom he felt closer while their family of four was still intact (with his sister Dorothy, three years younger)—did not entertain those kinds of views. People like him had the feeling part of them uppermost. They *accepted* life, accepted *themselves,* more than those like his mother, were closer to his own way of being, even though much of his mother's ways had been passed onto him.

That is what people said—certain traits were *passed on* as though a child was put together like a piece of handiwork.

Had his parents made a mistake in marrying? If they had not, he would have been unborn—a nothing. That was a curious thought, for he felt as though he had not been created at all, as though he had always *been*. If his parents had never married he was sure he would have returned to earth in *some* form, an idea that consoled him, though he had found it was not something other people were comfortable discussing.

Time, it was said, was curved, did not progress in a straight line—it flowed back upon itself. Which seemed to mean that the present was constantly becoming the past and did not really exist at all: only past and future merging together in one uninterrupted current.

That meant that the seeds of endings lay in their beginnings. If you knew how to judge what you saw, a whole life could be glimpsed at its outset—or at least by the age of ten.

His age the year it happened.

Trouble had been building for a long time before that. His mother was ill from something that kept her away from home for extended periods—a stay at a sanitarium and once at the seashore made her better enough to return but she was not as strong as she had been. As his father's drinking grew worse he was absent from East Dorset increasingly. The grown-ups tried to keep everything from him and Dorothy but they knew enough. Knew that something had to happen soon.

Late in the summer of that year his mother took them to Emerald Lake three miles north of the village and under a favored tree by the shore, where they had gone so often on very different occasions, told them what had happened.

"Children, your father won't be living with us anymore."

He would be moving to Canada in the far west, taking with him several men from the local quarry, and would not be coming back.

It was like a death.

He felt like someone who had been suddenly killed and for a short time lingers on, observing the end of things.

The moment separated itself from all the others he had lived, pulsating with a life of its own. It had ceased to be a moment in time and had become a wound of undiminishing pain. He seemed a different person from what he had been before the words were spoken, though he said nothing, and sat without expression. Questions would not cancel the moment, would only intensify its reality and reveal to his mother and sister his helplessness.

He was so alienated from himself, he was sure they must know. But perhaps they did not. Dorothy said a few words, he could not remember them; and his mother added a few, which he did not hear.

He felt he was keeping a pact with himself—or with his father— not to betray his reaction.

The bright day shimmered with unreality, as though he had opened his eyes on another planet.

He never knew the particulars of the separation, though the heavy drinking must have been involved in it.

A second, chilling shock followed with the news that his mother had filed suit for divorce, something almost never heard of in his world in that far-off year of 1906. But, suffering and shaken though she was, with legal advice from her father and from an attorney in the county seat of Bennington, she pushed it through, making it clear that her former husband was truly gone from them—from the area and from their lives.

Hurt, humiliated, shamed by her action, having lost face with friends and relatives, not to speak of his family, his father had fled to a place as far away as possible.

He and Dorothy would now be brought up in their maternal grandparents' house just behind the village church. After his mother had gone away for still another rest for her shattered nerves, she persuaded her father, Fayette Griffith, rich from stock speculation and the most prosperous man in East Dorset, to finance her medical training in Boston, where she wished to go to become an osteopath. So, unbelievably, in a very short time after his father had vanished without a trace, she too was going ... but meanwhile (he could not help noting) dramatically free of her various illnesses and restored to vigorous health almost overnight once the divorce was official and the Boston venture crystallized.

Both parents escaping from their family life, rejecting him, abandoning him when he most needed them. Both guilty, both failures, though perhaps his mother bearing the greater burden of guilt.

So he concluded from the painful whipping she administered in the last days before she left. In his unstable state he had behaved capriciously, speaking more sharply than usual, moving about with sullen, grieving looks, all of which, combined with some passing provocation, goaded her beyond forbearance. Seizing a large hairbrush, she had cornered him in his bedroom and not released him until he had promised over and over to mend his ways, striking him with such force, such *anger,* that as she beat him he wondered what had riled her so, what it was in him she wished to drive out, what he had *done* to make her so outraged. Was it only himself she was scourging? Or ... something else? Astonishingly—in swift, desperate lunges of thought— he was able to grapple with these questions even as she brought the hard brush down upon him again and again.

His *father* had loved him, he sobbed incoherently. His *father* had never spanked him.

"I'm your father now!" she cried, beating him again with a strange hostility.

Finally she had left him still sobbing. It was the only time either of them had ever whipped him. It must be that she was missing his father, was unhappy over the family breakup, and was taking her misery out on him. That must be the answer. He felt better. He stopped sobbing. After a while he would go to her, tell her he was sorry he had made her angry and would promise never to repeat it. By making her proud of him she would love him all over again and forget her anger.

His father's flight and his mother's departure were separated by several months but in retrospect seemed like components of one fateful action, like folds of a single leaf.

Constituting the first *moment* of his buried experience, the crisis that closed off one era in his history. A moment above all of *feeling*, of life being lived in the most acute, immediate way he had ever known.

In his beginning, his end. In the overture, the climax.

Both his parents had acted badly—that he knew in his heart. Selfishly indifferent to the two children they had brought into the world. But he still loved them, always would, could not accept the truth of what had happened, especially the truth of their motives. Instead, almost by instinct, he had quickly transferred their egoism and failure and made *himself* the guilty one, the one in the end responsible for the disgrace, the divorce-stigma, and his sense of being orphaned.

He banished flickerings of resentment and blame that passed across his vision and chose another role: one that burdened him with guilt, with anxious minglings of shame and self-pity.

After the initial shock had tempered itself in the channels of his psyche, his love for his parents held it all in check, acting as the solvent to everything else.

Indeed, had he loved them *enough,* the divorce, the *rupture* would not have occurred. He believed that he possessed enough love to convert any negative situation into a positive one. If the condition had not changed it was because of *his* failure to love as he should have.

In short their breakup may have been a punishment of *him* for not loving them truly, for not being better than he was, for being too selfish. And now they had turned from him.

He would fight back, would not rest until he had changed things—made them as good as they could possibly be.

He could not bear the thought that they no longer loved him.

He would write often to his mother in Boston, telling her of everything he did, his health or sickness, his grades in school—and since education meant so much to her, get grades to make her proud of him. From his letters she would know that he did not believe she had really gone.

It would be more difficult to keep in touch with his father but through the widow Wilson sooner or later he was bound to. Perhaps in time he could save up money from Grandfather Griffith's weekly allowance to take the train all the way across Canada to visit him and show by his love and joy in seeing him again that he held nothing against him for leaving.

He would never give up until he had brought them back into his life, until he himself had atoned for what had happened, paid for the unhappiness they all felt. And made them sorry for what they had done.

Until he had saved them from the consequences of their actions. Saved all of them, including Dorothy and his grandparents.

Often he dreamt of sacrifices he would make on their behalf, or of himself as affluent, his parents in need, saving both from destitution and misery.

But an emptiness remained and would not easily leave him. It never did.

He felt *used* ... not so much by them as by some unknown force manipulating them all.

2　The Tavern

Meanwhile timely challenges posed by Fayette Griffith, a perceptive father-surrogate who doted on him, assisted his urge to self-preservation. Such as the mystery of the boomerang, whose secret was said to lie with Australians alone.

"No American has ever made one. They say that no Westerner can." Fayette's old eyes glinted.

This Westerner could, he assured his grandfather, as he began six obsessed months when everything else was forgotten in his determination to equal the Australian feat, which eventually, after whittling and shaping and planing endless varieties of wood night after night, he accomplished.

Standing with his grandfather in the little churchyard behind their house, he flung his boomerang into the distance and with a cry of triumph saw it return to him in a flawless, soaring arc. He felt godlike.

If he could do this, what could he *not* do? He could be Number One in anything he tackled.

"'Will' is an apt name for the boy, Emma," Fayette told his wife. "I never saw such willpower in a lad."

"The boy is smart, Fayette," she agreed. "He can fix *anything*. He's jus' *smart...*"

From his little room upstairs, from whose windows he could see the trains passing in the night, he had gratefully heard them through the thin walls.

Then Fayette was encouraging him to study the violin: after repairing a discarded fiddle he found in the attic, he learned to play it on his own. And urging him to read, which he voraciously did, escaping into the world of books—precious hours stolen from sleep in hungry concentration by the light of a kerosene lamp, only half hearing the wail of the New York-to-Montreal express pounding northward on the western edge of town.

He soon shone at his studies, the sciences especially, eager to have his mother hear about his high grades.

His drive for eminence accelerated at Burr and Burton academy, a prestigious, coeducational, semi-private high school five miles south of East Dorset in the summer resort of Manchester. Situated on a hill at one end of town, the main building was a large gray stone edifice set among spacious grounds, overlooking the community. He boarded there during the week and on weekends took the train back to the Griffiths' house.

Putting to good use his power of single-minded absorption in anything that challenged him, he soon was a school leader...somewhat awkward at first in competitive athletics, but practicing constantly to perfect his abilities, tirelessly forcing his tall, agile, energetic frame to obey his will. Within a few months he had developed himself into the star of both baseball and football teams.

More significantly, he felt the students drawn to him *personally,* apart from his achievements. Since his parents' divorce he had made a habit of molding his disposition in the effort to charm others and in the process almost overcame his underlying consciousness of feeling apart from those he beguiled.

Driven to be first on the athletic fields, he felt the same motivation behind his social ambition. He would be the most popular student as well. In the absence of parental love, making everyone *else* love him.

Including the sons and daughters of privilege, students—often from distant places—born to wealthy, upper-class families.

His popularity brought him wide attention. When he was elected president of his class without opposition, he noted that it was not his natural abilities that had succeeded for him: he had improved on nature, he had *remade himself.*

Not least of all, he became first violin in the school orchestra and in the glee club cultivated a pleasant singing voice and an inborn love of music, which he believed he had inherited from his father—"who could sing, *really* sing," he told one of his fellows.

And did not forget to pass on the good tidings to his mother, making sure his father through the widow Wilson heard them too.

But subtly flourishing through all his triumphs ... a strong *ego*.

And always, no matter what he did, the feeling of apartness. Never escaping that, and aware that he had not.

His original sin. Always with him.

"It's not in the Bible o' course, Will," Mark Whalon protests mildly, almost for form's sake, his tone ironic, lightly irreverent. Mark and his grandfather Fayette are agnostics, both students of Robert Ingersoll. He reflects that the two men he most admires (after his father, of course), are both well-read free-thinkers.

It is the summer of 1908.

Mark, home permanently from the University of Vermont, is a good friend, the only one in the village he feels comfortable talking to about philosophy. Because of the ten-year age difference Mark serves as another father-surrogate. In addition, because of Mark's presence in the Wilson house the night of his birth, there is the continuing bond between them.

On this occasion they had been taking a country walk and discussing, among other things, reincarnation. Their walk brings them past the front door of the Marble Man tavern on the outskirts of East Dorset, an inviting prospect for Mark, who drinks a good deal, though never to the point of being a problem.

"Let's step in and rest our bones, Will..."

He follows Mark and, motionless as in a photograph, stands just inside the darkly cool, low-ceilinged tavern, the door shut behind him. Eight or ten men are present, half standing along the bar to the right, the others seated a short way off to the left at booths and tables. They look up curiously for a moment, a few nod their heads in recognition, then calmly turn away.

He is struck by the close, exciting atmosphere—the acrid tavern odors, the muted cheerful voices, the tinkle of glasses, the murmur of camaraderie. A secret, convivial, masculine world.

Mark has treated him to a glass of cool cider and ordered ale for himself. They stand at the bar. The bartender is a taciturn, benign-looking Irishman.

He sips the cider and looks around the room, goes to examine the framed photographs of sports champions on the walls. Several of the men, noticing him, smile, nod approvingly, bringing him into the circle of their fellowship. He passes a brief word with one or two who know him.

"Not seen ya much lately, Will..."

He feels a sense of oneness in the room, of mutual acceptance from everyone, a rough kind of affection in their eyes and voices. He sees that they slowly sip and nurse their ale to keep themselves at an ideal level of congeniality with their peers, which they must have had difficulty doing without the help of the soothing drink.

He returns to the bar, chats with Mark, again looks about.

He is caught up in a mood of initiation. A door swings open inside him.

This is his father's world, and this is perhaps the very place where he would have come on many an occasion, mixing comfortably with the kind of men now here.

The discovery of the arcane world of alcohol was also a direct link to his father, to his unknown life, to the realm he had inhabited.

That is why his father had drunk the way he did—to open himself to this sympathy, fellowship, oneness with other men. Perhaps it had been the only way he knew how to find it!

In Fayette Griffith's house there was no drinking of alcohol of any kind but here in this tavern in a moment of time it became identified with all that was good, affirmative, kindly accepting. With harmony, affability, quiet cheer. It made life a kind of paradise.

The moment had come. Something had shifted in him, some fateful change had taken place.

Some revelation had opened to him this day.

He hardly heard Mark when he spoke and answered haltingly. He wished he was alone, deeply alone, communing with his father or with the spirit of the past. When they went out again into the sunlight the moment had faded on one level, on another had already entered into the unexplored recesses of his psyche.

3   Lost Love

Because of his accomplishments at Burr and Burton he had attracted the attention of various girls, but his extreme reserve had kept them at a distance ... his shyness a reverse manifestation of his readiness, his craving, and his fear—because she was still unknown—of woman. With the spring of 1912, the urge to love and be loved had grown too strong to resist.

He and Bertha Bamford, the Episcopal minister's daughter in Manchester, a seventeen-year-old president of the local YWCA, and soon to be treasurer of their senior class, were drawn into frequent contact on class business, justifying their hours together, and making the passage of love into their hearts smooth and swift.

He did not consciously choose to be attracted to one type of girl rather than another but in the subliminal regions of his mind the effect was as though he had. What had guided him in his choice was the desire to love someone unlike his mother, who had been unable to give him the love, protection, and gentleness he needed—the true feminine presence in his life.

Sexual longing united to an innate worship of the feminine, embodied in one young woman radiant with virginity—that was his experience.

Since his mother's departure for Boston six years before, she had returned periodically to East Dorset, and each time he had noticed something growing, *manifesting* in her: when he embraced her on these occasions that new element seemed to block off the warmth and tenderness he expected.

It was as though she was mysteriously *unfinished*. His mother.

She would soon be licensed as a physician and would, she had told him, take no male patients.

The early feminists were active then and the realization that his own mother was one of them left him aching for the arms of love of another kind of woman.

Powered by his budding sexuality, more difficult to deflect now, his desires focused on the beauteous person of Bertha Bamford and the result electrified and overwhelmed him.

All his instinctive need to love his fellows was channelled into a passion—both sensual and sacred—for one individual girl.

In Bertha he found her femaleness linked to the service of her *spiritual* or *feminine* element ... though at a deeper level he intuited that he really needed the maternal *combined* with the feminine.

The result was like an intoxicating perfume almost unknown to him. It had to be this that a man worshipped in a woman, the awareness of some diviner presence, some strange depth of beauty and of higher consciousness that aroused in him the instinct to adore.

That she was a minister's daughter only enhanced both his longing and worship. In his imagination he thought she must come of superior stock, be of a higher quality in the seed that had produced her.

A girl with all the credentials. A true match for the boy who wanted to be Number One in everything—not least in the choice of the girl he loved.

The spring and summer months were wondrous. After the concerns of his young male world—scientific pursuits, mechanical triumphs, the challenge of *things,* and the turbulent cries of the sports fields—there was *this*.

He was transfixed, reborn, unbelieving. A new, other being inhabiting an old, familiar body.

Like spirit moving in matter.

Human love had raised the veil opening to the divine more than religion itself had ... though hitherto (thanks in large part to the anticlerical influence of Fayette Griffith and Mark Whalon) religion had meant little enough.

And his love was returned. Everyone knew it. School leaders, they moved in a golden aura, universally admired.

On the playing fields, she sat in the stands and saw him excel. Never had he thrown a ball so hard, striking out more batters than ever, and on the gridiron punting a football for new distance records. In the orchestra while she heard him play he seemed to draw deeper and richer harmonies from the violin.

When they were alone they held hands hesitantly and embraced with care, touching each other like revered objects.

They were almost too close in their virginal passion. Once he had surrendered to her he discovered how, in one respect, they were so alike. She was all feeling too!

He thirsted for self-sacrifice, for the chance to immolate himself on the altar of their love. He mitigated the horror of the *Titanic,* which had sunk in mid-April, by placing them on the fatal deck that terrible night.

He saw them embracing for the last time, saw Bertha refusing the chance for a seat in the one remaining lifeboat, saw himself insisting that she do so. She must *live*—live a long life, always cherishing the sacred memory of their love. And he must *die* to make that possible.

Yes, he was sure—without a moment's hesitation he would sacrifice his life for hers, would be *eager* to ... die for the immortality of love.

But he also sensed they did not really know each other, subtly intuiting limits to what was possible in the relationship.

"What are your plans, Will—after high school? What do you want to do with your life?"

Instinctively he knew he could not answer with the promptings of his heart. Instead, because of the *mood* between them—closed, self-loving—he spoke in terms of private ambition, of merely personal, material goals, of application to MIT and an engineering career. That he could not reply as he *truly* felt—and to *her*—seemed to signify something too uncomfortable to dwell on.

As they took walks among the hills past the spacious school grounds or sat on a bench overlooking one of Manchester's lakes, confessing their love once again, planning some day to marry, there was a hint of shadow, a distressing intuition of things he could not bear to think of, even as the shadow lingered.

"I have a sad and painful duty this morning," the school principal said, speaking gravely. He and his class were in chapel.

Unforgettable the place, the announcement, *the moment.*

"Bertha Bamford, senior class treasurer, daughter of the Episcopal minister and one of our most popular students, passed away suddenly yesterday in New York City. A successful operation brought on complications from which she failed to recover. Funeral services...."

He had *known* what was going to be said before the fatal words were uttered, known it with a stab of pain, a tremor of hot guilt in his realization of some truth silently, secretly operative in their months together.

Yes, he remembered that moment of certainty in the chapel. But *how* could he have known? There was no slightest sign that she was ill, no hint of any crisis impending. *Still he had known*—had anticipated the principal's words. And once again the question: why should he have felt such instant, unmistakable *guilt*?

It was *that*, almost as much as the shock of her death, which affected him.

And three days later, while carrying the casket with its precious burden out of the church to the cemetery, his mind seemed to reach some psychic comprehension of what had happened, seeming to perceive—if fleetingly, in corrosive spasms of enlightenment—the *why* of things. But as he did, once again there was the thrust of remorse and bitter self-indictment—as though, if truly possessing this occult knowledge ahead of time, he should somehow have spared Bertha the fate in store for her.

His self-condemning reaction made the fact of her loss too difficult to bear and almost at once plunged him into a continuing depression unique to him hitherto.

The only positive aspect of what had happened, if he could dare to think of it so, was that in the days immediately following her death the *strain* of his thinking—his compulsive, self-damning mental states— brought him to a preternatural level of understanding unlike anything he had known, filling him with awe at the operation of his own mind, at the further mysteries he sensed within. By comparison, his father's departure six and a half years before had induced unbelief, *numbness,* rather than the emotional gulf into which he was now cast, bringing his mind into such a pitch of tension that he seemed to penetrate the barrier separating ordinary knowledge from the actual truth of experience.

The result was that in pondering her loss and feeling again, in spite of himself, the cutting edge of his parents' rejection, he began to sense the working of some hidden, omnipresent force in his life whose designs were totally at variance with what normal expectations of people like himself might suppose.

Guilt was the common denominator in his response to both tragedies: in the first instance, guilt that he had not loved his parents enough while he still had the chance; now, guilt that *somehow,* in the depths of his mind, he had known that their love could not last, that it would have to end in the way it had, and that despite this secret knowledge he had said and done nothing that might have forestalled what had happened.

Though what it was he might have said or done he did not know.

He got up from the armchair in the studio and moved to the large swivel chair at his desk, to be close to his journal if the inspiration should seize him....

Even now the moment in the chapel came back again through time, unchanged, silent in memory.

Yes, he *had* known.

That was the time he had first begun to sense seriously that there *was* something uncanny going on in his life, those early anguished days just after his seventeenth birthday when he seemed to be turning himself inside out in the effort to understand and ... to accept.

And now he *had* ... understood a good deal of the mystery, at any rate, and accepted what he could grasp and assimilate—understood that what he had been put through over the first seventeen years of his life, what had happened and *not* happened, had gone systematically into *the making of an alcoholic personality* ... which—*apart from the discovery of AA*—seemed to make no sense at all. For what reason would he have been *worked over* in order to become a ripe victim for alcohol when he should turn to it?

Only in conjunction with the revelation of AA was it a feasible possibility.

What had dawned upon him was the incredible fact that not only AA had been part of the design from the beginning but that he had been singled out, also from the beginning, to be its progenitor—and then in turn AA was to become *his* parent, as it was to this hour, watching over him, protecting him, warning, coaxing, threatening, reassuring him constantly over the years, coercing him—for the sake of so many—into an absolute sobriety.

It had all been foreseen, predestined.

He had had something to do with it, but more had been done *to* him. He had merely been the raw material shaped—*mis*shaped—into an appropriate form for serving the inscrutable intelligence behind the whole drama.

Some are born great, some achieve greatness, some have greatness thrust upon them.

Yes, greatness thrust upon him....

The long preparation, everything being used, turned into capital, making its contribution to the overall mixture, year after year. Only slowly the knowledge growing—knowledge of what was going on, but because of the strangeness, the *disbelief,* never assimilated until now. But undoubtedly the first significant flash of insight into the process in evidence during those late November days when he discovered Bertha was gone.

Even earlier, in uncomfortable fleeting moments, he had realized—*felt,* rather—that though a bond of love held them they did not sufficiently know each other, that on other levels they were different.

Very different.

Bertha before they had met had led a sheltered, circumscribed existence and was happy with it: *that*—he knew now—was what she was. She did not feel shackled, rebellious, did not feel her father was narrow or unjust.

She was a minister's daughter who loved her father and the year was 1912.

She wanted a conventional life; he, a larger-than-life experience.

She loved the bounded, the known, the traditional; he, the unbounded, the unknown, the new.

Hers was an accepting mind; his, an independent, skeptical one.

Her need was for a prescribed kind of happiness; his, for something else, he did not know how to name it: for greatness perhaps.

To become as great in his self-realization, in tapping all his potentialities, as humanly possible. But he knew, as he had known that day when they were walking near the lake overlooking the football field, that he could say nothing of this to his beloved.

More concerned with a continuance of the undisturbed serenity they had known than with the truth of things.

But the power behind his life, and behind hers, *was* concerned with that truth. As events devastatingly revealed.

So, despite their secret vows one day to marry, when he had found a job after college and was able to support her, they were not meant to marry and, as had become shockingly clear, would not be allowed to do so.

If they *had,* he would have had difficulty supporting her or even holding a steady job for very long, once he had begun to drink. She would have had no real idea of whom—or *what*—she was marrying. And neither would he. As his addiction took deeper hold, slowly beginning to wreck everything, her lofty, idealistic love would suffer a grievous trauma, never to be healed. She would not, he knew—regretting it now, but accepting it too—have the stamina to persevere and outlast the demon. Bitter disenchantment would destroy their love—a fate truly worse than death for both of them—leading to possible suicide for either. Or else she would have to leave him, and her abandonment would be crushing.

No, not to marry, not to live together.

Rather, she was there to give him for the first time the experience of love, romance, poetry, ecstasy—and then by her death to wound him terribly: the wound necessary in the formation of an alcoholic, obsessive character for life to work with, or work *over*. She was there to be the agent of the pain, the new and greater emptiness, to make him still more vulnerable, more than ever susceptible to *feeling,* to throw his nerves into a new pitch of tension and grief, to *change* him from what he had been ... or rather, to continue the movement that had been going on, only to accelerate and intensify it now.

She was there to deliver, by her death—by its suddenness, by her *vanishing*—the *coup de grace* in the creation of a personality which, when the time was right, would be made to succumb to alcoholism and its enslavement as irresistibly as any man ever had.

In the process her rare and precious life becomes a pawn on the chessboard of *his* life. *Hers* is simply snuffed out, with no qualms, no hesitation ... to make a vital contribution to the extraordinary mixture he was being fashioned into for reasons even now not fully known— though guessed, uncomfortably.

But the mission accomplished. He is left *mutated,* easily manipulable, at the mercy of forces that will act upon his psyche with magisterial inevitability, reshaping him further, using him at their pleasure.

And, he thought, to the emotional crippling, the fatal mixture, add one very large *ego* ... produced perhaps in the very effort to *survive* the crippling, both prior to and after Bertha. Hence this too, the flowering of the necessary egoism, was doubtless foreknown, foreplanned ... even his efforts at survival no more than predetermined jostlings of adjustment, only further locking him into the master structure.

He absentmindedly ground out his cigarette in the large glass ashtray on the desk, next to his copy of the Big Book, sat for some time looking vacantly out through the plate glass windows onto the green panoply of summer all about him.

Then his thoughts shifted and he sat up, more alert now.

The formation of ego—he had never seen it so closely. The mixture: the maiming, the great well of feeling, the secretiveness, the naked sensitivity ... always the *apartness*. And the ego, with time waxing stronger, *fed* by the apartness, the sin against life, the living lie. Finding itself *different* from others no matter what it did to effect the contrary, it *justified* the condition, as it justified itself… every ripple of difference from others only increasing its unknown life, leaving it unresistant to sudden influences or changes that gave it an identity—vulnerable to potions that let the burdened individual under its sway escape into *another* consciousness.

Filled with a sense of awe, he reflected for a moment in the quiet studio, picked up his fountain pen, and tried to capture the essence of these ideas in his journal: the effort of concentration, combined with his excitement, exhausting him. After a time, in a different strain, he added another passage:

> —I seem to see much of what has been going on—*in* my life and *to* it. But in all truth, perhaps because of the very existence of that egoism whose origins have grown clearer than ever, I have never adjusted to it well, am not much reconciled. The pain of those years is still alive now.
>
> Perhaps because "I" and the phenomenal mixture are still too much *one,* do I think thus. With more detachment from what I have been molded into, then—then—
>
> Another way of stating the problem: *my emotional nature* is still powerful, still rules. I can live with this, have for a long time, should be able to do so for the rest of the journey. But it would be a better journey if the *feeling* faculty had been made subject to the higher will, the enlightened understanding. I cannot doubt that…

He turned again to the past to find more answers, however painful. Nothing could be more unpalatable then the prevailing state that had prompted the exploration.

Expectantly he lit another cigarette.

4 Pilgrimage

The aftermath continued the work of grinding him down, *remaking* him into an image of someone unable to cope with his emotions or endure the inclemencies of life.

His grief went on unbroken month after month, drawing on constantly fresh reserves of bitterness and questioning. The depression was abnormal—he *knew* that, but could not seem to exhaust it. Someone else would have suffered for a reasonable time—*his* mourning continued for two years.

His grades dropped and he was absent from class as often as not. He abdicated his responsibilities as student president. Sports could not arouse him. Nothing could, except the violin; in some fashion the mysterious harmonies of music were able to assuage a measure of the hurt. He clung to it as his only solace.

He was thankful winter was the first season to get through; its silent Vermont bleakness, its death of life, struck a grimly responsive chord, and it had no personal associations with Bertha.

With the spring it became obvious that he would not graduate because of academic failure, which left him indifferent. It was his mother who reacted. Preparing to cajole or demand, she rushed to Manchester to pressure the principal into allowing her son to graduate, and failed in her objective.

His depression won no sympathy from her, since she well knew its source: the death of a teenage girl who had infatuated him. *That* did not seem reason enough for the way he was carrying on. He knew that part of her indignation at the principal was due to her impatience with *him* and part of his own misery was his realization that in failing at school he had once again failed *her*.

He found himself remembering his father persistently. A yearning to see him again, as an instinctive way of healing the wound, rose in his heart, to the extent of making inquiries about train fares and schedules to Montreal and thence to British Columbia. Even as he acted thus he knew it was unrealistic. Since he did not know if his father wished to see *him,* it would have been impossible to make the first move: a negative response would have been unbearable.

But in his intense introspection that first year after Bertha's passing, internal reality had a credibility of its own, strengthening his inward-brooding tendencies, deepening his taste of aloneness, as though preparing him for something ... he knew not what.

Meanwhile despite his desire to do nothing there were things to be done, credits to be made up, colleges to be investigated once graduation from Burr and Burton was official. In the summer he worked in desperate fits and starts but managed to regain the necessary credits for the diploma.

An unexpected distraction was the chance to accompany Fayette Griffith to the fiftieth anniversary celebration of the Civil War battle at Gettysburg. Fayette's participation in the great conflict on that far-off day at the mid-point of the war made the visit exciting and instructive.

But it served only as a diversion. The current of his hidden life continued unabated, absorbing him, carrying him along without resistance. Strangely, he did not feel the time was lost, as though he *had* to pass through this limbo ... despite his mother's admonition to think of his future and her stressing the need to organize his life around a sensible ideal instead of allowing it to fritter away in useless daydreams.

Once he had graduated she insisted that he come to Boston to live with her and Dorothy, which, in the fall of 1913, he did. At the high school in suburban Arlington outside of Boston he prepared himself for the entrance examination to MIT. All that winter he studied, taking no part in the school life around him, and feeling no sense of progress in his studies. His mind could not concentrate for long. His will to *make* it concentrate was weak, his overall reserve of energy low. Which only angered and dismayed his mother.

"If nothing else will galvanize you, Will, I wonder why *shame* does not! Think of what I have had to go through to earn my medical degree—one lone woman in a man's world! I wonder if you are truly my flesh and blood."

Her words were like salt stirred in the raw wound of his pain. How little she seemed to think of him, how little there was that he could do to please her!

Knowing he would fail the examination, which he did, was hardly able to answer a single question confidently.

As an alternative his mother arranged for him to apply at Norwich Military Academy in Northfield, Vermont, where he was accepted without difficulty for the following September. Norwich had been a satisfactory alternative because of two prime advantages: its reputation for discipline, and its total absence of young women to beguile her wayward son.

With that, he was free to return to East Dorset for several months. It was a relief to escape from the tense, nagging atmosphere his mother created, which only brought him new infusions of guilt. Just the chance to pass the summer without having to be responsible for anything beyond his own existence calmed him ... though at the same time gave him occasion to fall back into depression and to reopen his grief.

He craved something that would, in spite of himself, take him to a new level of experience: instill in him hope where now was gloom, energy where now was inertia.

Life—still shaping him, working in its own timetable—made him two distinct offers during that last beautiful summer just before the war began. That they came at this particular juncture seemed to indicate that the timing was part of a prearranged plan.

• • •

The first was Lois Burnham. He met her in the idyllic setting of Emerald Lake, where he was spending much of his time in long recuperative solitudes.

He soon had known the basic facts of her background—that she was a college-trained city girl, the oldest of six children born to a successful Brooklyn surgeon and his wife, who brought their family every summer to Manchester's high country and eventually discovered the tranquil beauty of the lake. A budding romance between Dorothy and one of the Burnham boys led to the first meetings with her in earnest that year, though a passing early contact had been made the previous summer.

Lois ... four years older, like a young mother to him almost from the first, as though each sensed the keynote of their relation ... dark-haired, dark-eyed, slender, of medium height, vivacious, flashing the pert, ironic smile with which she confronted life, an educated, self-possessed young female with social graces new to his rustic experience. Greatly drawn to her even in the midst of his still potent identification with Bertha's image, he wondered what she thought of him, as they cautiously moved toward a more significant stage in their attraction.

Something else gave him food for wonder—the curious fact that Lois' father had built their family bungalow on the precise spot close to the lake where long ago his mother had told him and Dorothy that their father would be permanently gone, the traumatic moment from which he had never recovered. He could not help but interpret this to mean that where the first experience had brought him a kind of living death, something was inherent in the Burnham cottage that would bring him life—Lois herself.

In the place where he had been shattered, now he might be healed.

And Lois Burnham would be the healer.

In sanguine moments he reflected that, though probably conscious of her age, she did seem taken with him—aware of his need of her helping hand, her strong maternal nature, and as their tentative courtship began he saw that she was listening to him more and more, *struck* by him perhaps, less concerned with the age difference, very likely unable to explain what it was that drew her to him.

Something she had simply *known* ... as though some intangible power had enlightened her?

The same power that had brought them together—that had caused the Burnhams to build where once something had been destroyed, to bring him joy where once there had been a source of never-ending sorrow?

The other offering was his father.

It was eight years since he had seen him. He had been a child then, was close to manhood now. In a rare letter to his widowed mother a few months earlier his father had inquired about "my son Will," with a hint that he might like to see him again if he could bring himself to make the trip all the way out to Marblehead, British Columbia.

He was immediately excited by the chance to see his father after so long and as the means of possibly shaking free from his prolonged enervation. After further letters were exchanged, making it clear just where Marblehead was and how to reach it from the trunk line of the transcontinental railroad, he was ready to set off. The widow Wilson and Grandfather Fayette would share the expenses.

He said nothing to his mother about the plan, though she knew of course, and she herself said nothing, at least to him. While the arrangements for the trip were being made she was fortunately busy with her medical studies in Boston, freeing him from what might have been her discouraging presence.

Armed with a large, oilcloth-covered bag brimful of sandwiches, fruit and pastries contributed by the two grandmothers and Dorothy, and a sturdy leather valise in which a map of Western Canada he had gone to Rutland to obtain was packed in his clothing next to a special journal-notebook bought for the occasion, he rode and slept in a train rolling endlessly over farm and prairie like a journey into the past century. Still overcast by the memory of Bertha, though fading, he realized the new, strengthening relation with Lois Burnham had given him the assurance he needed for the encounter ahead.

He was traveling westward to find his father, to discover the parent he had never truly known. To demonstrate not only his love and affection but also his freedom from reproach over what had happened those eight years ago.

And by this act of pilgrimage to bridge the great time-gap between then and now, between the innocence of the past and the conflicts of the present, and change their lives, *revise their histories,* recreate them in a new and better image.

He would do for them what they could not do for themselves: forgive and forget, make amends, and be reconciled. The thought of all this constituted another *moment* that changed his life. Even in the act of considering these possibilities he felt changed.

The image that moment bequeathed was as servant of Life, as champion of others, liberator of those who could not free themselves. Or would not.

During the days just before his departure, reaching a peak of recognition the day he left, he had seen on their faces a mingling of admiration, wonder, sadness, envy, encouragement, gratitude, hope, and self-rebuke flickering there by turns, like shadows of the mind, almost too swift to be apprehended. They seemed to be seeing him in a bright new light—as their emissary and representative.

He long had known that Fayette and Emma Griffith, steadfast teetotalers, had shared their daughter's shock when they discovered that Gilly Wilson, known to them all their lives, had become a problem drinker—worse perhaps, whatever it was about the divorce he had never been able to learn. In any event, the stigma had been branded on his father's name and he had chosen the option of flight and silence as his response. But over time their sympathies had moved steadily back toward Gilly and now they thought that Emily may have behaved too rashly.

Year by year, relieved and grateful, he had felt their change. Hence when he had expressed his desire to go to Marblehead he was not surprised at their support... at the same time their unspoken assumption that his mother would be omitted from discussion of the plan and if possible told about it only when the train ticket was paid for.

Still more supportive was Grandmother Wilson. Her own husband had been a heavier drinker than Gilman, had indeed been an alcoholic who, after years of addiction, had found release in some kind of religious experience that, according to family lore, transformed him overnight. His death a few years later was from other causes.

She had never truly absorbed the disgrace and what she thought as the injustice of the divorce and the subsequent loss of her son from her life. By Will's decision to go west to see his father he knew she would benefit in ways she could never relate, though the gratitude and admiration in her eyes spoke plainly enough. Fayette was willing to finance everything but she insisted on paying half. It was obviously an investment that in some secret way would bring her a special return. Indeed, the whole idea of his westward journey seemed to fill her with an unusual happiness. She told young Will that he must be some kind of family angel. "I'm sure you take after your father."

And he thought that was true also, had always thought so, despite the firm set of his mouth—a marked Griffith trait.

Dorothy, too, was part of it. Everyone agreed it was not appropriate for her to go with him because for one thing it might seem to represent some kind of defiance of their mother, which neither was prepared to make, nor had any reason to think of doing. But her enthusiasm for the plan was spontaneous and sustained. Now, at the age of sixteen herself, she was perceptive enough to bestow upon her "brave brother" the benediction of her moral support—not the least of the treasures of comfort he brought with him.

"I wish I could go with you, Will. I'll pray for you every day."

He knew they would always remember this trip, his mother included. Even before he had left, it had assumed the character of a legend, a landmark that divided periods of family history. Now again the thought of his role as emissary for all of them thrilled him with pride, glowed in him as a white, pure flame, while the train pounded on relentlessly toward his destination.

After the long life-negating span he had suffered through, it was a unique experience. He sat in his seat restless with waves of fresh energy surging through him.

The *moment* deepened, intensified, grew more complex, life-changing, character-forming even as it came to pass, on the instant seeming to become a permanent reality in his psyche.

• • •

His undertaking the trip at all was his first independent, unequivocal action in nearly two years. Once again he felt grateful for Lois Burnham, whose cheerful energy and optimism toward whatever life might offer her had obviously touched him. After he returned to East Dorset he would tell her about the trip if her family was still at the lake. If, as she thought, she had returned to Brooklyn he would write to her at the address she had given him: 182 Clinton Street.

There was something else that had caught his attention. Since he had started west he was able to turn his mind away from the memory of Bertha and to *forget himself:* to be absorbed by entirely new modes of thought. Instead of dwelling on his private problems, as he had been doing for so long, he was now thinking of his father, of his grandparents and sister, of Lois, of the meeting in Marblehead, of Norwich Academy, beginning—though in no consistent way as yet—to think vigorously again of the future as opposed to brooding on the past.

After the final transcontinental stop at Nelson, British Columbia, there was the overnight stay at a rough traveler's hotel where, before falling into a restless sleep, he made an initial entry in his virgin notebook:

"We're often unaware of the important days as they transpire. As Europe, now at war, is gearing up for some tidal cataclysm, so my own history may this day be undergoing a momentous experience—"

Then an early-morning appearance at Nelson's fog-shrouded lakeside wharf to board the paddlewheeler plying the seventy miles up Kootenay Lake between the close abutting, snow-capped crags that seemed any moment about to crash into the low water, taking nine hours to reach the northern terminus in Lardeau, a meager railroad hamlet, then the timed connection with the one-track local the last eight miles to Marblehead through similar country, heavy with trees— pine, evergreen, hemlock, juniper—thickening at the shoreline, in places fruit orchards, cultivated farmland and meadows, but the terrain little like Vermont, more immense, less touched by man, everything more sublime, more *grand,* and all of it domesticated somehow, made familiar by the realization that his father had doubtless ridden through these fields and forests and tiny settlements and they had perhaps become as known to him now as Vermont scenes once had been.

Then it was Marblehead, a remote quarry-fed community of workers and their transient dwellings and all-purpose cookhouse and machinery and vast marble pit dug out of a mountain side, the great cliffs towering over them with threatening immediacy ... and amid the end-of-the-day windup of activity, the one in charge, the man with the big house on the hill above the quarry whom he had come twenty-seven hundred miles to see, who now stood on the country depot platform to meet him, the tall, graying, sun-browned, slightly stooped and shambling, warily smiling, watchful-eyed man with his powerful weathered hand out-stretched—

"Let me look at you, Will. You're tall as me and twice as good-looking!"

In the heavy stillness of the silent quarry, and the great, close-looming mountains, he lay on his bed in the hilltop house and from time to time in another room heard the sound of his father stirring. Lying on his back, he studied the moonlit shadows on the walls and ceiling and it was as if they were lying down to sleep in the East Dorset house in a time long lost ... amid the enveloping silence the faint return of sounds and night murmurings, like those at home. He had met his father again and was sleeping in his house and what he felt was as unfamiliar as though he had become someone else, or awakened in a dream and found himself where he was.

Past and present, answering to his desire, mingled strangely.

They spoke a great deal, the first day or two. His father introduced him to the stone-dusty workers, who greeted him with shy smiles.

"He's come all this way to visit and he's the next Christy Mathewson!"

The door of memory opened. He remembered all the evenings they had played ball together, how much it had meant to him. The closeness, the love he had felt—the security. And the songs his father sang. Again he heard his husky, tenor voice, the reedy organ accompaniment of his mother on the ancient melodeon. Captured forever like a photograph of time gone.

But it was gone.

What he had come to find he knew he would not.

Something was missing, he did not know what. There was a great *divide*. Which did not seem to distress his father: the gulf between them *his* doing. Probably he was not even conscious of it. Or, if he was, he might think it perfectly natural.

But he kept his own counsel, was just as casual and friendly. He must show no sign of criticism, reveal nothing at all of his disappointment. The letdown. No hint of blame—no *awareness* of such—for having abandoned him.

From his science readings he remembered that every seven years the body's cells were renewed, in effect creating a new body. That seemed to have happened with his father: he was changed, *different*. Or perhaps it was not so much that he had changed as that he had always been in essentials as he now was.

What made the discovery painful was his genuine friendliness, his natural curiosity about his son's accomplishments, his honest pleasure on hearing he had been a star athlete and was registered to enter a known military academy next month. Had such news relieved his fears that his disappearance long ago had sown other kinds of seeds?

The dust on the men's clothes and on his father's, and in his hair, made him wonder if men that worked among stones and marble became stone-like themselves. Just as farmers came to resemble farm animals, their gaze stolid, obtuse.

Despite the humor, the healthy good nature, there was something hard and unpliable in his father.

Something incomprehensible.

He had brought with him recent photographs of Dorothy and himself. On the first day he offered them to his father, his gesture awkwardly constrained—he must not seem to be forcing them on him.

"She's developed into a real beauty. She'll be a heartbreaker!"

The photographs were lying face-up on the kitchen table, cluttered with other things, including newspapers, and had been there from the first day.

His father would soon be remarrying. The woman was called Christine.

Now he guessed what had prompted the inquiry about himself in that letter some weeks before. The expectation of another wife had rejuvenated him, freeing him of the past, giving him the spirit of independence he needed to write the letter.

That was a component in his congeniality. When you had found a new source of happiness it was not difficult to be cheerful with everyone. On the other hand it was equally clear that his natural goodness was there to be tapped if, as he did at the moment, he had the incentive to do so.

Whatever happened, he would strive to keep the contact open: perhaps eventually—despite the obstacles known and unknown—persistent signs of filial concern might persuade him to change himself into a more positive image equal to what the contemplation of marriage had done.

The advent of a woman in both their lives at about the same time had made all the difference. Not only for his father. For himself too. His relation with Lois of course had not advanced so far but already had provided him a strength and confidence he had not had. If this was a favorable time for his father to receive the visit it was also favorable for himself to have made it. Again, he was struck by the appearance of some kind of design—in all the lives impinging on his. Without Christine and without Lois the visit would not have been made.

As well, in both cases they were acting, almost in rhythm, independently of his mother, who hitherto had been for both the dominating influence: for his father, a source of continuing resentment and bitterness, which at last he seemed to have cast behind him; for himself, the loved, possessive, strong-willed woman whom in spite of his pride he had adored, hoping in vain on countless occasions to do something to please her and make her want to embrace him, her only son, with her love.

He still loved her and always would but now he was beginning to feel within him a larger capacity for freedom and self-reliance than he had known. It was not a great deal yet, but with this visit he felt it would increase.

Yes, bound to increase. Not directly perhaps....

"As in a chess game," he wrote in his diary-notebook, "a move in one corner of the board has the secondary but intended effect of exerting influence and change in an entirely different area..."

The mountains haunted him, like mountains in a dream.

Their impenetrability and towering vastness were like a mirror of his frustration, a reality never to be scaled or understood. Something immutable, mysterious, unconquerable. Now his western journey seemed an attempt to penetrate what could not be known. Locked away in the mountains lay the secret he had come in search of.

Even the men who worked the quarry seemed elfin, phantom figures laboring in the adamantine rock, in the process making themselves more like the stone they cut.

His father too. The impregnable ranges seemed a symbolic expression of his personality.

As the week progressed he had the sensation of stepping into the milieu of another lifetime.

Reincarnation.

Gropingly he tried to commit his anxious thoughts to diary entries. Not too successfully. The effort, however, reinforced his belief in rebirth, of having lived before, of returning again after this life.

"It is a belief not only in reincarnation but a growing faith that life itself is like a dream, a truth disclosed with force during dramatic moments when all our expectations are seen in a shockingly new light...."

Reincarnation led by natural stages to at least the possibility of *predestination.* Was the unbridged gulf between his father and himself *intended* to be such, part of a *design,* including the flight from Vermont eight years ago, not even excluding the divorce? Was it all fated, part of some mighty prearrangement?

At times like this it seemed plausible.

But if so, the *purpose*? Its relation to him? To his future?

Everyone had been talking about the war in Europe.

"Eventually the U.S. may be drawn in but if you play your cards right you'll be out of Norwich ready for a lieutenant's bars. People will look up to you, Will. You'll be an *officer*—an officer and a gentleman! I'll really be proud of you then."

Smiling in his hearty, rough-hewn way.

He waited for the word, the truth. It never came. Rather, a truth did reveal itself, one he had already accepted. No revelation emerged to change that.

When he had been there a full week it seemed time to leave. His father rode the eight miles by rail with him to Lardeau, where the steamer was waiting on schedule.

As they stood on the landing in the early morning light his father extended his strong, brown hand. "This visit has meant a lot to me, Will. It was *big* of you to come...."

He waited until the last passenger had boarded, then turned to go.

"Keep in touch..." Those were the last words he heard before his father left to make his way back to the little depot. He walked slowly, but with an air of freedom, like someone relieved of a burden. When he reached the depot, not far from the landing, he waved. His gesture was that of a man untroubled, unreflective.

He tried to assimilate these impressions into the substance of the earlier ones. He did not feel as downcast as he had guessed he might. The overall feeling was mixed, muted.

It was worth the effort to have come.

He waved a second time as he moved to find a place at the front of the steamer, the morning sun bright in his eyes.

5 Relapse and Recovery

The dramatic absence of female students at Norwich impressed him enough to find a place in his notebook a few days after enrolling:

"It is not only Bertha I miss, but also her sisters in beauty and charm. Here the heavy masculine element universally dominates. As I had known it would. Never before have I realized how drawn I am to the fair sex and how admiring of their estimable qualities!..."

In two months he would be nineteen. He felt the sway of nature peaking in him during that whole first disoriented year. If the sexual was not the only factor in his restlessness it was a powerful one: a deep emotional nature craving *some* comfort, and able to find none in the purlieus of a military academy.

Lacking a psychological support for his life, he brooded over the visit to his father, the inconclusiveness of which distressed him and made his attempt to assimilate the experience difficult. He had thought to find in a renewed—a *recovered*—relationship with his father a true center for his life, a focus for his churning emotionality, and had failed. Nor did his mother represent an alternative. And Bertha was gone.

Lois Burnham? There was a season's difference now. She was still far away, taken up with her busy New York life, their happy last times together at the lake no more than a memory. After returning from Marblehead he had written to her but her answering letter was a shade more lukewarm than he would have wished. Had he exaggerated her interest? Projecting upon her his own needs and desires? He might well be. He would try again in a few weeks and meanwhile look for something favorable to tell her about his career at Norwich.

Which was not likely to happen. Living in a flux of irresponsible drift, he was not adjusting to life in his new environment, was simply refusing to adapt, and knew it.

It was painful to discover that his athletic talents, so successful at Burr and Burton, were ineffective at Norwich. When he attempted to compete on the baseball and football teams he was hardly noticed, and even his music failed him here. His passion to excel was balked at every turn, though he knew also, without being able to act on the knowledge, that here he was not bringing to his activities anything like the single-mindedness he had exhibited in high school.

At Norwich he was just one of a hundred and fifty cadets, no longer Number One in anything. And the unkindest cut: the fraternities had ignored him.

With a sudden shock to his vanity he realized the versatility his grandparents had praised in his boyhood and his brilliant record in Manchester prior to Bertha's passing had been mere juvenile and adolescent achievements. Among eighteen-and-twenty-year-old competitors he was an also-ran. And there was as yet no *new* arena for his ambition, no way yet glimpsed that would restore him to a position of eminence.

He was not blind to the immaturity of these sentiments but could find nothing to take their place. He simply *had* to be first. It was the only way he had so far discovered to compensate for what life had wrought in him. His ambition he saw as an attempt to best life on its own terms ... even though in the process he would expose himself to strain and the risk of depression, and always to the feeling of standing apart from others: that mood which, in times of success or failure, was never far from consciousness.

But if apart, at least *ahead* of them....

Caught in this web of influences constricting his impulses and sapping his will, he began to suffer attacks of depression and anxiety, feelings of breathlessness accompanied by chest pains. Sometimes there were other kinds of seizures, like heart palpitations, which terrified him ... reducing him to the humiliation of desperate prayer to a God in whom he had no special wish to believe.

He became a familiar visitor at the college infirmary but received no lasting help because only the conditions were being treated, not the complex of causes, and—more mysterious still—the reason why it was being brought to bear upon him with such intensity.

Sleepiness attacked him throughout that first semester. No matter how long he slept or how often, he could not soak himself in forgetfulness enough ... by this addiction nakedly expressing his desire to be somewhere else than where he was, do away with normal consciousness in great draughts of sleep, wipe out the self he was, the life he knew, in favor of the luxury of perpetual drowsiness.

How he studied at all mystified him, but he kept his grades at least in the passing range, often nodding in class or arriving late with no time for breakfast.

Sleep became his drug, his solution to the indignities and unceasing expectations which life demanded of him: not only in ways that might be understood but in ways unfathomably obscure.

Why struggle, when the anodyne of oblivion and the drifting opulence of drowsy solitary hours in his little room at Norwich were available? The importunity of life, its *unremitting* character, oppressed him, and he was responding with the gamut of illnesses that perplexed the doctor at the academy, most of all by *sleep,* which condensed the significance of the rest.

The Christmas recess brought a brief respite but no change and no escape from the inevitable return to Norwich. The ice and snow and the winds howling down from the mountains mirrored his mood. As he trudged through the outskirts of the village he saw himself as someone whipped not only by life but by raw Nature, finding in the wintry symbols a grim satisfaction.

He looked up Mark Whalon but was reluctant to describe the real nature of his Norwich experiences lest Mark, whose good opinion he prized—who was always praising him and predicting great things for

his future—think him weak and irresponsible. In his heart he knew
what the truth was, knew that the role he was playing led nowhere.
But knowledge of a condition was one thing, the capacity to act on
that knowledge something else again.

Early in the second semester he slipped on a sheet of ice in front
of his dormitory and had a bad fall, injuring his arm. Once again he
went to the doctor but this time insisted on his mother—"an osteopathic
physician practicing medicine in Boston," he had explained earlier—
treating him. It meant going all the way to Arlington, the crowded
suburb northwest of Boston where she lived and had her office, on a
busy cobblestoned street where bell-clanging trolley cars ran, but he
went almost eagerly, comforted in the knowledge that at last he had
reason to have her treat him, at the same time becoming the first male
patient she had ever accepted!

After she had performed a few simple manipulations of his arm
he quickly felt better, almost from the moment she put her hands on
him and made her adjustments.

As he was preparing to leave he felt her large, dark, steady, beautiful
eyes narrowing upon him in a fixed, skeptical gaze, showing affection
clouded by an element he had never understood: something intact
and remote, serving her own interests, disdainful of others' motives.

"… You're not malingering up there? I've had reports—"

He denied everything. His grades were reasonably good, weren't they?

"Surprisingly—with all your ailments. But sometimes people seem
to get ill when they want to—"

Or have to.

"—And now with this fall you took—"

Did she for a moment think—?

"Just don't be a malingerer, Will. Appreciate your advantages—"

And disadvantages?

"—and strike the anvil hard!"

Instead of striking anything hard he wanted warmth, and easement of his misery.

On the way out the door opening onto the Arlington main street
he turned back mechanically for a moment and saw the pretty, well-formed,
blond-haired office secretary—her hair, like his mother's, tied in a

bun—passing a typewritten page to her for her inspection. Standing in the inner office, the door ajar, they did not see him. As she stood waiting for his mother's comment, there was a worshipful look on the secretary's face. Just before he turned awkwardly back to the street he saw his mother nod with affectionate approval and touch her fondly on the head.

A new wave of confusion seized him, and a sense of dismay. For some reason, anxiety clung to him all the way to the North Station.

What he had witnessed seemed full of meaning, perhaps was important for him to know. But *what*? Why was he suddenly thinking of that day just after his father had left, when she had whipped him so angrily? What was the connection?

He returned by train to Northfield but hated the thought of resuming his status as a nobody on the small, too-disciplined campus, and in the middle of winter. Hence the pattern continued, except that now the Norwich authorities, puzzled that no physical cause could be discovered for his problems, suggested he withdraw for the balance of the second semester and after a long rest return in the fall. He agreed to this, as did his grandparents and—reluctantly—his mother.

For weeks there was no improvement. East Dorset overpowered him with the ghosts of memory—his father, their early family life, his Manchester years, his love for Bertha, his sense of a golden past lost forever in the cruel obscurities of an alienating present.

Symptoms of his unhappiness returned. A local family physician treated him, again with no improvement or understanding of what the trouble was. Worst of all, his depression—fed by his unshakable sleepiness, his craving to have as little consciousness as possible—hung on.

"... I seem to feel no desire to live," he wrote in his notebook. "Nor do I particularly care why I feel so."

Once again he seemed at the mercy of his own nature, his excessive capacity for emotion ... as though he had the soul of a woman in a male body.

The coming of April enabled him to get out of the house more often. He walked great distances in all directions and gradually some of his energies revived. He spent time with Mark Whalon, once he had thrown off the negative impulses and could present to his friend more of the image he expected.

When his depression lifted enough he wrote to Lois again and received a prompt, spirited reply, reanimating his psyche. Full of hope, he wrote a third time, once again she answered quickly, with the impression of something in her letter he had looked for in vain last fall: a genuine interest in him, a desire to see him again at the lake this summer, and the tone of a young woman openly fond of the young man she was addressing.

A surge of excitement possessed him. He literally counted the days until she and her family returned to Manchester and to their bungalow camp on the lake. A powerful psychic current seemed to be vibrating all the way from East Dorset to Brooklyn.

The attraction he felt towards her, though strong and genuine, somehow seemed different from what had drawn him to Bertha and from what he had tentatively felt for one or two other girls earlier. It was another kind altogether, although he could not define or quite grasp what it meant.

The feeling of fate, of predestination, the mood that had so often gripped him, usually in ways that made him feel overburdened, often pressured beyond understanding—that was what it seemed like again, but this time it brought more auspicious emotions in its wake. Something to be embraced and affirmed rather than merely accepted. Something that would lift him up, and not weigh upon him with mysterious omens.

After the physical and psychological seizures he had gone through he could not deny that he was turning to her to *rescue* him. He was not ashamed to admit it. Isn't that what a woman could do for a man when it was required? *Wasn't a man's life a kind of fury, a self-oppression,* needing the nurturing, the maternal understanding and care of a good woman to protect him from not only the temptations of the world but from something worse?

Himself.

True, he did not feel for her what he had for Bertha but perhaps that was just as well. He needed the maternal now more than the romantic; the caring, dedicated woman more than the merely beautiful ... though there was more to Bertha than beauty alone: her bright affectionate amiability was a still more striking factor in his memory of her. But she lacked Lois' *force* of character, her strength, her sheer *maturity*... that most of all had drawn him to Lois Burnham. Being four years older had helped, as had doubtless her experience gained as the eldest of six children.

He recalled how vividly he had felt a sense of guilt when Bertha had died—unreasonable, groundless as it may have been; yet he was sure it had contained a measure of truth: his intuition that by loving him she had bought an early death as the price of her love, and that somehow he had known or sensed this from the beginning.

With Lois it was entirely different. As far as he could determine he felt completely free of any such misgivings. Now he wondered, all the same: what was it that had left him free of any hint of guilt or uneasiness toward *her*? It must have been that very maternalism that was her dominant feature, of which he stood in such need at this juncture—combined with her self-sufficiency, her keen enjoyment of life's slightest pleasures, and, he guessed, her acceptance of life's challenges.

A woman so developed seemed *protected,* was—at least potentially—a direct instrument of life's purposes. Such a person was so valuable to Life from so many standpoints that her individual existence could not be spared—could not, in all likelihood, be *taken* from her, as he had seen happen two and a half years before with Bertha.

No, the guilt, the hesitation, any residue of misgivings—none of this was there for Lois. He felt free. And from the tone of her letters, she seemed to feel the same way. Even though they would be meeting again in a few weeks they were writing every other day, and the letters on both sides were growing longer and more intimate, showing less and less desire to hold back, such as had still marked their behavior last summer at the lake: more and more on the brink of confessing their love.

Somehow, without his noticing, one by one all his medical problems had vanished. One morning he woke up and found himself free of them. Even before their reunion, she had healed him.

Rather, by dwelling on the prospect of her entering his life with power and readiness he had healed himself.

Early in May, off the coast of Ireland, a German submarine sank the *Lusitania*, a British passenger ship with more than a hundred Americans aboard, outraging public opinion and bringing the country a major step closer to entering the war against Germany.

He remembered the sinking of the *Titanic* almost exactly three years ago—how he had visualized his self-sacrifice to save Bertha's life, and the deep consolation this had brought him. After the *Lusitania* he had difficulty recalling in any believable sense that sacrificial passion. The realization shocked and saddened him. It was as though he was dwelling in a different zone of consciousness, a new time-warp, wherein the emotions and motivations of three years ago—which seemed so far away—were painfully inapplicable.

He also discovered he was moved by no such feeling for Lois— for the good reason, he brooded, that his pure love for Bertha had been the prerequisite for his projected life-sacrifice on the deck of the *Titanic*. What he felt for Lois, genuine and powerful as it was, did not, in its essence, generate the fervor of romantic self-effacement.

He had known this before and accepted it as the *present* requirement, as the ideal condition for him *now*—and therefore more to be embraced than what he had felt three years before. It was the unexpected rekindling of this knowledge in conjunction with the *Lusitania* sinking that jolted and surprised him.

The discovery of how much he had changed, without his acknowl- edgment or awareness, stunned him. Even as his love and need for Lois grew day by day he was melancholy with the realization that the year of his love for Bertha, like a fable in his memory, was already consumed in the awakening energies of his life, propelling him onward to a kind of existence, perhaps, different from everything he had known. There still lingered in his mind an ache of nostalgia for what had been— as though he might find a way to keep both realities strong and living within him through the oncoming days.

Knowing also there was no such way.

• • •

A warm, clear June afternoon. No one was about, which had not always been true the other times. Now, if he wept, no one would see, which seemed a kind of violation of the sanctity of the moment.

Beyond that, he had found it too painful, too desolating, to come often. It had been a long time since his last visit. After today—it was sad to know—he would not have to come back again.

He had purchased a bouquet at the florist shop next to the church and now he placed it carefully on the grave. He read the inscription, the dates of her birth, felt again the hypnotic fascination of her name carved in stone.

At the funeral, when the casket was lowered into the grave, he had thought he was burying with her his own life. Now he knew that he had buried the part of himself that had loved her, buried his past.

He did not really think *she* had been buried, only her body. She herself was elsewhere, in other realms, perhaps even now preparing for still another return to earth. Because of her orthodox upbringing the idea of reincarnation had offended her, and he had spoken of it with her only once, but by now she would have discovered its truth.

The real girl he had loved—her essence—lived on within him. It was on that he meditated, with that he communed—not with the body that had succumbed to mortality. Dwelling within, she would remain a permanent part of his life in an essential way, like the image of beauty.

Lois would soon be arriving at the lake. She would be the future, as Bertha was the past. Even before her arrival, he felt the new power, the organic unfoldment, occurring. He had had to make this visit to a shrine of his past before the process had advanced any further.

The graveyard, like his thoughts, was very still. For a long time he sat there, motionless, smelling the flowers, the grass, the odor of death, watching bees in their swift flight, hearing bird cries in the summer distance, vaguely from far off the thin echo of human voices.

Gradually his mind, sunk in its sphere of stillness, charged with silent feeling, grew free of images. He was alone. He tried to feel that Bertha was there with him but could not. Instead, he thought of her, gently, hopelessly, with troubled concentration, thinking of their time together, of what she once had meant to him. His sense of aloneness deepened.

Farewell, he thought. I will not come again.

He rose unsteadily, grateful that no one was yet in sight. He walked away toward the train station. He had not wept.

6   The Pact

On Labor Day at Emerald Lake, after a warm holiday afternoon of songs, canoeing, and picnics on the grass, Lois re-baptized him. Wearing an attractive blue dress and a straw summer hat, she drew a cup of water from the lake, sprinkled a few drops on his bare head, and in a mock-formal voice intoned:

"I baptize thee in the name of the God of history and his feminine counterpart, abjuring the down-East designation of *Will* as unseemly for someone fated to do great things, who henceforth shall be known as *Bill Wilson*!"

They laughed. It sounded right. *Bill,* he now was.

Aware of various pungent food odors mingling with the fresh scent of grass, they walked slowly hand in hand beside the water, near Lois' rustic-style, green-painted tea-and-refreshment arbor set up at the north end of the mile-long lake, which she had operated all summer to keep herself busy. Most who had gathered for the music of a small brass band collected for the occasion had left; those who remained were strolling about in the fading light, relaxing on the grass, or sailing on the lake.

It was just a month since their engagement. Lois had kept it private; he had told Mark Whalon, his father-confessor, but so far no one else. The secrecy intensified its meaning, gave it an aura of special import. He thought all precious things should enjoy a period of nondisclosure befitting their unique character, not suited for a casual mixing with the mundane world, a too-hasty sharing with those not party to the compact.

Perhaps he should have waited longer before informing Mark. The problem was that he had already spoken to him glowingly about Lois, had received steady encouragement, and it had seemed almost inevitable that he would speak of the engagement as well.

Within sight of the arbor stand, which Lois, with his help, had closed a few minutes before, they sat down and half-listened for a time to a nearby quartet harmonizing several of the musical successes of the season.

"Let's sing with them, Bill—I love to hear you when you sing!"

He chimed in readily, enjoying her fine voice as well.

> We were sailing along
> On Moonlight Bay
> We could hear the voices ringing
> They seemed to say...

They saw in the distance Dorothy and her boyfriend Rutgers Burnham, joined by another couple their age, setting off in a shiny, black 1913 Model T Ford in the southbound direction of Manchester, where a touring Broadway vaudeville company would be putting on an evening holiday entertainment at the summer stock theater. He and Lois would have gone too but Lois had to prepare for her departure tomorrow morning to get ready to assume her fall employment as a secretary-coordinator at the Brooklyn YWCA. This was their last time together for the summer and they were reluctant to limit it in any way. After the long day they were contented to stay behind, enjoying one another's company. Idly they waved at the Manchester-bound young people, then turned their attention back to the harmonizing quartet.

> There's a long, long trail a-winding
> Into the land of my dreams...

"What about *your* land of dreams, Bill?" Lois asked in a soft, challenging tone, smiling shyly, yet questioningly, at him. She had placed her straw hat on the grass next to her. "What do you dream of?

After all, we're engaged now—I have a right to know! What do you want to do—*really* do? How do you want to spend your life?"

He recalled, from three years ago—again that interval of time when comparing events of his life with Lois and with Bertha—a similar question Bertha had put to him, and his inability to answer as he would have wanted. Now it was different. With Lois he could confess his most secret dreams, longings he had scarcely been able to acknowledge to himself.

Yes, he hoped to become an electrical engineer after graduating from Norwich, but he wanted more out of life than merely material success. There was so much suffering and misery in the world, so much ignorance, loneliness, fear, so much hatred and selfishness, that any decent, thoughtful person should want to make *some* contribution to ameliorating conditions, want to do *something* to help the world as an expression of his common humanity, almost as a duty to life itself.

That, he told her is what he chiefly wanted to do—to be of service to mankind in some way he had not yet discovered and to make that ideal paramount in his life.

Her face registered a look of thrilled satisfaction.

"And I shall accompany you on that journey! You have touched something in me that speaks to my own deepest nature as well!..."

With a pang he knew he had not told the *full* truth about his hopes and dreams, had not acknowledged that in his desire to help others he wanted to be *preeminent* in doing so—be the world's Number One humanitarian! He had pulled back from the whole truth ... lest she draw away from him, too suddenly shocked to learn something unexpected about his real nature—or that part of it so egregiously self-centered.

"... I too feel the same, Bill. I too wish to be of service to mankind in this sorrowful world, so that when the journey is over I will feel I have *lived* and not merely occupied space for my allotted years. But to be involved *together* in that kind of life is particularly exciting to contemplate, do you not think so?—"

More than anything it was.

"—Oh Bill, I have felt from the beginning something strange about us—something unusual, truly *different*—as though we are meant to live out our lives in that kind of way, and that we have been brought together to make it possible for such a joint work to be undertaken. I thought much of this even last summer and then again this past spring when we began to correspond, but this summer it has all come to a head.... Bill, let us cherish this moment of truth to guide us forward, to throw a light of illumination on our path." He squeezed her hand in response, gazed into her eyes dancing with their excitement. "There is something else, Bill. I didn't know how to mention this, and even wondered if it was appropriate that I should, but our present mood has convinced me. What I mean is—well, since last summer I have had the notion—the conviction, rather—that your life is very special somehow, just as you yourself are—not only to me, who happens to be in love with you, but as you are, in yourself, apart from my own feelings ... that you are fated to play a very unusual role in the world. I have thought that you are a man of destiny, Bill. I wonder if you yourself have not thought the same thing—have you?"

While he pondered his answer, the image of Mark Whalon and his lifelong faith in him had flashed into his mind.

She had raised such enormous possibilities that he did not know what to say, did not dare to say anything, for whatever he said would be inappropriate. She took his right hand in both of hers and squeezed gently, thrilling him with happiness, reassurance, gratitude.

The strains of another ballad reached them from the harmonizing quartet:

> I care not for the stars that shine
> I dare not hope e'er to be thine
> I only know I love you—
> Love me ... and the world is mine.

He stretched out on the cool grass, placed his head on her lap, and felt her slender fingers gently massaging his neck and forehead, as though banishing all negative, obstructing impulses from his brain and impressing upon it the ardor of her own conviction and faith in him.

Let love through her hands, he thought, reshape me.

The moment, all the moments with her, had a dreamlike quality— not as with Bertha, when *love* was the dream, but in the sense that *life* was. With Lois it was as though they were players on a stage and the power behind them, writing the scenes, was almost felt at times ... the way he intuited that they were drawn together not by love so much as by some other force, or motive, that seemed to point to some reality outside them quite as much as to the two of them.

With melodic quietness her voice continued.

"Sometime around the middle of last summer was when the change came for me—when I began to *see* you for the first time. Before that, you were part of the *group* we moved with, you were one of the *natives* it was good to talk with to help get a feel of Vermont and the rural life. It was when you told me you were going out to British Columbia to see your father whom you hadn't seen in most of a decade. *That* made the difference because I knew the background—you had told me some of it and Dorothy filled me in on the rest—and then of course this summer you have confided in me more than ever about your family and your school experiences. When you told me, confirmed by Dorothy, what you were planning to do right then—knowing his rejection of you, his indifference at least, his abandonment of you and Dorothy—knowing all this, I didn't find in you a hint of blame or resentment, only sympathy, affection, compassion, and hope that someday everything would be better. Then to be willing to go out there with no more than the barest encouragement, I could not believe it. And when I realized it was *true* I then and there decided you were the man I wanted to marry. I don't know anyone who could have—or *would* have—done it."

She pressed her fingers gently, probingly, into his brow and along the back of his head, as though seeking some answer in the conformation of his skull.

"And your mother! It is only a little less remarkable what you have done *there*—how you have been towards *her*. I have read between the lines of what you have been willing to tell me about your relationship with her and heard more from innocent Dorothy and I *know* she has not been ... all that she should have been—in fact, well—let us just leave it at that, though frankly I have been surprised and more than a little shocked by what I have guessed the truth is—and yet everything you say about her is kindly, forgiving, always making allowance, always giving her the benefit of the doubt—even *admiring* her! That really astonished me—your admiring her in spite of everything she has done and failed to do—"

He stirred under her, shifting his position slightly, ingesting all her thoughts, letting his silent attention speak for him.

"—Well, I concluded, if that is how he treats those who have mistreated *him,* how would he be likely to behave with someone who planned to do good to him *all the time* and who would make it her business to—would make it her private religion to do so!—"

He felt consoled, filled with a kind of bliss. He squeezed her hand.

"—Yes, I decided to *marry* you when I heard about your trip to the west. I couldn't let such a promising man get away—I would not likely meet his equal again. *Marry* you—because you knew something I didn't and others didn't either, perhaps didn't *know* you knew it. There's a Persian saying that goes: 'He who knows not that he knows not is a fool—shun him. He who knows that he knows not is a child—teach him. He who knows not that he knows is asleep—waken him. He who knows that he knows is a wise man—follow him.' Your description, Bill, is the third one: 'He who knows not that he knows is asleep—waken him.' And of course it will be the experiences of life and your response to them that will ultimately waken you. But life with the right woman, who lives only to serve your best interests and in so doing discovers her own—that *also* will help waken you!

"Yes, you knew something, or were on the *verge* of knowing something, and I wanted to be in on the ground floor when you finally came to know what it was you really did know! I felt you were open to mysteries, secrets, closed off to others. *You would be a great man,* you had been singled out by the powers-that-be for that fate. Actions speak louder than words. Acts *alone,* I believe, change us—and on that occasion when you made your pilgrimage to your father—as well as your behavior, your *psychology* toward your *mother*—on that occasion you performed in such a way that the true nature of the actor was suddenly, brilliantly revealed. By that one action you changed me forever. You acted as only a great man could—rather, a great man in the making.

"*Who would need someone—who would need a woman, the right*

woman—for that 'making' to bear fruit. I wanted to live close to someone who knew what you knew—knew in your unplumbed depths—and *was* what *you* were. That is what a woman looks for, my dear Bill—did you know that?—to meet and love a great man, a man of truth, a man capable of the memorable, rare action and therefore *a man capable of everything*—that's what I suddenly felt about you at the end of last summer ... *and to play a role, a necessary role in his self-realization.* May I be worthy of the privilege that has been unveiled for me!

"You seem to respond to Life out of a center different from the way others are motivated. Apart from what you plan to be and do, you could be a saint, a philosopher, a prophet, you could be anything at all. *Nothing can be predicted about you.*

"You are one of those who move to their own music, who walk by the light of inner illuminations. I believe you will be famous some day, once you discover—once *we* discover, I mean—the work you are called to do.

"But fame is not why I wanted to marry you—and actually *prayed* that it would come to pass! It's true. I was *so* certain that it was meant to be that I felt perfectly clear in my conscience praying over and over for you to come to a recognition of the same truth that I had. And you have!—" She ran her fingers slowly, passionately through his shock of hair, breathing deeply as she did so. "—No, fame is not why I wanted to marry you. It was rather the chance to be close, to *live* close to greatness as it evolves, to a destiny in the making, in the act of realizing itself! What a privilege that will be!..."

Her thoughts filled the horizon of his mind and her eloquence left him silent. There was nothing to add. Again, anything he said would be inadequate, off the mark. Silence was the fit response—acknowledgment thereby of the awareness of some great presence there with them, the power behind it all.

But even as he thrilled to what she had said and the conviction with which she had spoken, he was reminding himself that he didn't have to speak. His weaknesses, fears, hesitations, grandiosities—his unrevealed ego—would speak for themselves. She would discover all of them soon enough. Let her continue a while longer with the image she had of him. He could not bring himself to disenchant her.

But perhaps he could not even if he tried.

"... Let us both dedicate ourselves to that task, Bill. There is no time to lose. Let us not wait until we are married, because that may be five years away. In spirit we already *are*. Let today be the first day in our new life!"

With an intimate, mothering gesture, she pressed his face softly, yet insistently against her abdomen. He could feel her muscles contracting with pleasure and affection, pressed himself deeper into her body, as though into her womb, to lose himself in her nurturing womanhood.

They held the moment for some minutes in an intimate silence in which they communed with each other on levels deeper than language. A kind of perfection enclosed them, bringing them closer than they had ever been. He seemed to lack nothing, felt complete, free of all misgivings. Lois had become his conduit to the universe, to love, and to himself.

When gently he turned his face upward, seeing her dark hair silhouetted against the dimming light of the sky, she traced the shape of his head again with her fingers, lingering over each of his features with loving curiosity, as though seeing them for the first time.

In a different tone of voice, but with the same throbbing affection evident, she spoke: "One thing, however, my fine youth—you are not in danger of winning any beauty prizes! Yours is the kind of face that people describe as having *character*—real Vermont down-home character!—And you know why—it's because all your good looks are inside, invisible to everyone except those meant to know the truth. *Handsome is as handsome does!*"

He laughed softly, kissing her hand, holding it against his eyes.

The three-mile walk to the village had never seemed so short or his stamina so inexhaustible. Still in the aftermath of one of the golden moments he had known, he felt his life changing even as he strode southward. He sensed, as part of the revelation, a world of energy around him—all of Nature imbued with a current of life almost palpable, a vibrant mystery, a vital essence flowing and streaming through everything, through him ... an actual presence of some kind, something timeless, beyond even Nature herself, perhaps beyond life

... part of the same mysterious current whose presence he had felt today at the lake, particularly when he had heard in Lois' voice the reverberation of some rare truth he had never before experienced.

She had said things about him no one ever had, articulated intuitions about his future which he had hardly acknowledged even to himself, and done it with such conviction that it seemed as though the voice of truth itself had been speaking to him this day.

How great was a woman's faith in a man, how much good it brought him, how much influence she could wield in his life!

He felt an intelligence pulsing in nature—or through nature—in answering counterpoint to Lois' thrilling words, felt an awareness of destiny pouring into him with each stride he took. Could it be true that his life was in the control of fate, of some mysterious providential power behind all human affairs?

As he strode tirelessly on, his spirit reached out in an embrace of the oncoming days. In a tremor of ambitious longing for the future to happen *now,* he felt himself expand, aglow with sanguine excitement. He had not felt so strong and purposeful in the three years since Bertha had died. And, again, it was the presence of a woman who loved him that made the difference, that brought him back to his life after long months of indifferent living. He felt he could—*and would*—achieve anything he set his mind to ... *Love me and the world is mine.*

With their clandestine pledge they had experienced a double source of secrecy. The engagement and the pact. The one would soon be known, the other never known to anyone but Lois and himself. It seemed to connect him to a higher reality than that embodied in the engagement and even in a marriage. It joined them to the world of things destined, under the sway of providence and fate. Not only his own life but his relation with Lois, the prophetess of his life. The pledge they had made linked them with the power *behind* life, for whom, or for which, even Life was merely the means for working out of its own inscrutable Will.

The whole encounter today had constituted another moment that changed him and sowed the seeds for still further change in the months to come—the period when he would be throwing himself into the challenges posed at Norwich in order to make up for all the time he had lost. Another moment never to be forgotten.

Lois thought that *she* was fortunate. But *he* was the fortunate one. To have such a woman as spouse and helpmate and to feel that she was one of the marks of destiny in his life, that her presence had been mandated by the controlling powers in the universe.

Before today he had clearly recognized many areas where he had much to gain from such a woman in his life, but now one other asset was added: he would have as his companion a woman brighter than he, one who knew more about him than he did himself!

He was *glad* he had told Mark Whalon about the engagement. Earlier today he had thought that divulging the news so spontaneously had been an immature reaction, as though he was telling him that, since he was engaged to be married, now he was a man and was ready to stand on his own two feet, wouldn't have so much need henceforth for Mark's patient mentorship. But Mark deserved to know of this vital step he had taken not only toward maturity but towards the attainment of everything else that life might offer. Now there was meaning, reality in his life for the first time. Finally he had made a conscious commitment to the Real, to the True. The Real was the relationship between himself and Lois in all its potentialities for him ... for both of them, of course. But Lois was already closer to the heart of Life. *He* with the engagement *was announcing his willingness to unite himself with that which he lacked, to become that which he was not yet.*

He had at last taken the step toward becoming a man which for so long he had needed to take. The change was under way. Already within him the seeds were stirring with harvests of new and unknown life.

Much more than his name had been changed this day....

Yes, more than his name.

Seated meditatively at his desk next to the picture window, he vividly recalled that day and the walk back to East Dorset. It was difficult to single out, of the dozen key moments in his life, *the* one of all, since each in its time was appropriate for the needs of the occasion, each had its own characteristic aspect. But that day was surely one of the greatest. It had shifted the scales of his life dramatically from what had been to what would be. It represented a rite of passage from delayed adolescence to young manhood, so that after leaving Lois at her bungalow early in the evening the feeling he had, of his life changing almost under his hand, was a valid and confirmed experience. It was one of the mountain peak moments from the top of which he could see the country of the past and, through a polychromatic mist, the stretching mysterious topography of the future.

While often his sense of being caught up in the play of unknown powers had oppressed and bewildered him, this time—the coming of Lois in so inevitable a manner—they had given him an opposite emotion: one of joy, gratitude, and energetic acceptance of anything they would see fit to direct his way.

For there was no doubt that Lois had come by the will of the gods, for a very definite purpose, and given illuminating conceptions of what it was they expected her to do and be.

Not only by the manner of her advent was this made clear—but also by its timing. When he had finally come to terms with Bertha's memory, at once Lois was there to comfort and reanimate the stunned, retreating personality he had become by the spring of 1915, after those two disoriented semesters at Norwich ... the woefully unsteady, unpromising young man of nineteen that he was.

That there was a design was certain. And if a design, then a Designer. If a drama, then a Dramatist.

And then the question: how much of the script had already been written? How much room for our free will?

Nursing his cigarette, he watched the film of his life unroll in the theater of memory, the sound film with its voices rising up to consciousness, like a voice he heard that night in New Bedford ... at the scene of the next moment in the drama.

Was there any doubt that *that* deserved its special niche in the pantheon?

7 A New Self

The voices were predictably similar—the bantering voices of young men, tinged with malice, on the whole friendly enough: "Not drinking, Bill?" As long as the context—usually at a military installation—remained the same, and emotional factors did not vary greatly, he had no difficulty deflecting their rote challenges, clinging to his long-held faith in the generational wisdom that "on his father's side of the family" there had been a drinking problem extending well back into the depths of the previous century—a faith that by December 1917, in New Bedford, Massachusetts, had become a fixed doctrine, an integral part of his reality.

But on this particular day at, of all places, the stately stone Grinnell mansion on County Street, not only the physical setting was different but the psychological forces playing upon him, in combination, stronger, more troubling than he had known.

Here was not only a new kind of situation in which to fend off the ironical inquiry about his nonalcoholic bias, but one that left him feeling strange to himself, dreading the consequences.

It was a state of mind all the more disconcerting after the steady rehabilitation of his self-confidence at Norwich ever since the Labor Day epiphany two years before. Once again, as at Burr and Burton, he had been able to make himself dominantly popular by an act of sustained will. Now, with Lois Burnham the inspiration of his drive, he had the incentive to do so; had improved his grades, notably in his chosen field of electrical engineering; and to help defray his tuition had earned money playing the violin in a school orchestra at local dances.

More dramatically, he had displayed a talent for leadership that caught the attention of his Norwich military superiors, an aptitude that proved still more significant after the country entered the war in Europe and he, along with his class, was sent to Plattsburg, New York, for officers' training. There, because of his Norwich experience and the rigorous discipline he had not only grown used to but actively coveted, he advanced swiftly toward recognition from new commanders.

He found that a peace-time military career held a great appeal and for a short time seriously considered pursuing it when the war was over. The sanctioned ordered life, quieting to one who had lived with too much disorder, the rhythm of a soldier's days and nights, the yoke of regulations, which others chafed at but which he took to as balm for his soul, the rule of a living tradition, the thrill of saluting and being saluted in return, the hierarchy of responsibility and privilege, the power in command, the splendor of bowing to a law greater than yourself, the ecstasy of leadership in front of a company of marching men—drilling, *shaping* them ... at dawn the clarion call of *reveille,* bracing himself for the day, the feeling of creating a personality with each morning, and at sundown the haunting requiem of *taps* as the bugler unfurled across shadows lengthening over the parade ground his slow-dying *vibrato* evoking memories of soldiers gone before and of battles long ago, all the glory and the sadness of military life caught in his throaty elegy, with thousands drawn up motionless, attending as to an unearthly music, in a silence unbroken over the entire post....

In short, an army career would provide him with the stabilizing influence he craved, with a definite place for him, perhaps in time a high place: a world where skill and merit would be rewarded, where he would have ample chance, as he had already begun to do, to show his capabilities. It would offer him self-fulfillment and permanent freedom from his cross of feeling inferior. He would be appreciated for what he was, a man among men—valued, needed, trusted. In time what limit would there be in such a future?

Dreams of valor on distant fields warred in his mind with his hope of a long exciting life lived out to the fullest with Lois.

He could see himself surrendering to the military option, and it was tempting to contemplate for the years ahead.

Tempting—but in the end not possible.

If he was alone, he would not hesitate. But he was not alone. He had found his life-companion. He could not bear the thought of her being forced to live in a succession of army bases all over the country in environments that would be so essentially alien to her spirit, her inclinations, her dreams.

By August he wore the bars of a second lieutenant in the Coast Artillery and was assigned to Fort Rodman just outside New Bedford.

Service in the heavy artillery would gratify his scientific bent, but he made his choice only after hours of anguished soul-searching over the fact that it was not one of the more dangerous branches. Lois however applauded his decision. "You have chosen wisely," she wrote. "Your intellect is so insatiable to *learn,* to *know,* that you had to pick a branch where it would be exercised at least adequately, and I think you have done that."

His misgivings persisted nevertheless. "Temperamentally," he brooded in his journal, "I am just not suited to the infantry, the 'queen of battles', breeding-ground of heroes. Perhaps I lack the courage...."

Once at Fort Rodman, however, the challenge of the new posting and the excitement of the times absorbed his energies, fed by anticipation of Lois' next visit to New Bedford, which was as often as she could make them. At Rodman his demonstrated flair for leadership was renewed, once more gave him the opportunity to excel among his fellow officers and to catch the eye of his superiors.

Meanwhile the gibing gambits of army comrades continued— "*Still* not drinking, Bill?"—but he had learned to respond, by reflex, with answering banter, turning occasions of potential distress into exercises in self-possession—and the show, at least, of nonchalance. Until the afternoon at the Grinnells', a most unlikely environment to begin with.

• • •

A fruit drink clutched uncertainly in his hand, he stood tensely and somewhat isolated—sober, guarded—in a corner of the large, richly appointed drawing room the Grinnell family had made available to younger Rodman officers and to selected young women of New Bedford to entertain them.

He remembered the first few weeks at the base when, after settling into his quarters and new routines, he explored New Bedford, sometimes with Lois, often alone, striding about the old manufacturing city, once the center of the whaling industry, now with its museum, its ancient streets, its statues of embattled mariners, its backward-looking nostalgic air, as though in tribute to its once-potent decades. Everywhere he went he was greeted warmly, with admiration and respect, as he strode about in proud awareness of his shining role, his uniform clean and freshly pressed, his boots polished, his spirit contented.

When he came to the County Street district he felt stabbings of envy as he gazed almost furtively at the houses of the wealthy, imagining the type of cultured lives they must be leading behind the walls of those hedge-protected mansions, finding satisfaction in the thought that in time he himself might be living in such a house ... while uncomfortably aware of the conflict in his life-goals: his ambition for a splendid home in the best part of town and his other ambition to be of genuine service to the world.

What did he *really* want? *Both,* perhaps. By having the house, and being *able* to have it, he might conquer his feeling of inadequacy among the wealthy and cultured classes, achieve inner wholeness, and independence, and *then* be able to serve humanity?

Was he fooling himself with this kind of reasoning?

At any event, what he vividly recalled from those early weeks was that of all the houses he admired through the haze of envy and desire the most impressive was the gray, granite edifice of the Grinnell family, in whose spacious and elegant reception room he now stood, nervously balancing a glass of fruit juice while the phonograph played a succession of popular war songs and half a dozen couples danced on the gleaming maplewood floors, from which two large Oriental rugs had been removed for the day.

> Keep the home fires burning
> While your hearts are yearning...

A silent butler efficiently kept the guests in a ready supply of alcoholic beverages and a variety of snacks on a buffet table, which included a mountain of tender white crustless sandwiches, a revelation after his long East Dorset experience of rough dark bread. In an adjacent living room another group, while the phonograph was being rewound, took advantage of the pause to sing in harmony around the grand piano:

> Smile a while, you kissed me sad adieu,
> When the clouds roll by I'll come to you...

Other couples moved between the two large rooms, greeting newcomers, heading for the buffet. There was youthful laughter joined to the music to add to the air of excitement, with an undercurrent of anxiety felt not only by the officers but by the sympathetic females who did their best to distract them from what was their real purpose as army officers. Dancing with the young men, the girls granted them more liberties than they might ordinarily, out of respect for the danger to which they soon might be exposed.

Despite his unease, his self-reproach for having come at all, he could not but admire the implications of the gathering: the fairest daughters of the community, led by the Grinnell women, taking pains to serve and comfort the young warriors soon to depart for foreign fields. Quietly he assumed his share of the adulation being showered on the officers.

> I have a rendezvous with death
> At some disputed barricade...

A reflection that did little to reduce his tension. On the contrary, the sight of the others, male and female, enjoying themselves in so opulent a setting, only intensified his misery. The orphan-complex, he thought, with its strain of self-pity and anxiety, compounded by the country boy's awkwardness in the presence of *class*. There wasn't supposed to be class distinction in America—when, in fact, it ruled everything, all the more keenly felt by its supposed nonexistence.

Four months an officer—but not yet a gentleman! His father had exaggerated. They could *make* you an officer but only if you had the energy and knowledge to devote to the task you made *yourself* a gentleman. Which he was so far from having done.

Some seemed born to it—the natural aristocrats, the well-bred, the deeply cultured. Someone like himself would spend his whole life gazing at *that* kind of class, and never really be a part of it, could only by wealth or some special personality gift he did not have, attempt to link himself to it and pass himself as one of them ... which of course *they*—like the people who lived in this grand house—would see through and thwart him when he least expected it.

By loving and wanting to marry both Bertha and Lois *he* had, to some extent, done that very thing—attempted to make himself part of a world that would have been beyond him without their help. Lois, especially, had belonged to an upper middle-class family whose way of life and standards, and the very speech they used, stamped them as coming from a sphere radically different from what he had known. After the engagement was eventually announced he had visited them at their request in their Brooklyn home, and though they had done everything to make him feel comfortable, and Lois herself had been flawless in managing the subtleties of the situation, he had always been uncomfortable with them—even with *them,* his in-laws, the family of the woman he loved.

With a family like the Grinnells, and people of *their* level, he could never hope to be free of the weight of his discomfort, his constant apprehension that he would do or say the wrong thing, with the result that he did and said nothing.

What he felt about them went still deeper. It had to do with some violation that people like the Grinnells everywhere had committed in feeling they were superior to others, in setting themselves apart not only by their houses and visible displays of wealth but by the words they used and even by their very accents. *That* was what disturbed him, their sinning against some common humanity that all men and women shared.

The compulsion to be superior! Even his own mother, despite her modest educational background, had this tendency, as he had seen on many occasions—most notably with his father, whom she never for a moment thought was her equal!

And this trait in human nature magnified, made intolerable in the rich and cultured, the darlings of fortune from birth.

So why had he come?

To see how they lived, to walk in their hallowed houses and imagine they were his, to breathe their air and see if it would not make him, *also,* into a better, finer, more sensitive, accomplished young soldier-aristocrat! Unquestionably his wearing the uniform of an artillery lieutenant had been part of his motivation. He had walked about the streets of New Bedford in that spirit, and had come here in a similar mood, needing to project an image of youthful military poise and confidence, of natural inborn leadership, and in that drawing room filled with all the things he wanted to own for himself he had been utterly unable to!

No, the character, the real depth, was not there—only his constant need to stand out, to be something he was not. And the proof that he *was* not came when even with the advantages of his status as a young lieutenant about to go to war he could not escape his limitations, his anxieties, his fear of these people, his peculiar, automatic resentment of them, even as he desired to be like them! His unease, he sensed, was a reflection of his desire to be *as they were.* Someone who did not want to feel that way would not envy or resent, would be able to take them or leave them without his inevitable pattern of reactions.

Why couldn't he simply remain noncommittal, *non*reacting when he encountered them—accept them for what they were, perhaps even try to understand them, remaining content in himself, *with* himself, as Mark Whalon and as his father, also, could do—each superior to him in this essential way? Why could he not *live and let live* with the rich and cultured classes? Were they intrinsically wicked, without any redeeming qualities?

He well knew why he could not. The same reason, always the same.

He lacked the stability in himself to enable him to do so.

The problem was not *them* at all—*he* was the problem.

His makeup, his personality, *what he was*—or what life had shaped him into.

That was the problem....

Always apart from others: his natural condition, his instinctive posture toward the world, for all his practiced gregariousness.

That was the problem.

Standing ever apart, assuming his private mantle of *superiority* as he judged everyone. With his democratic philosophy of everyone being as good as everyone else—but *he* had to be Number One! Best in everything—best athlete, musician, engineer, officer, the most popular, the most imitated!

How explain *that* inconsistency?

He could not, made no effort to do so, his confusion only deepening, adding to his tension.

He rebuked himself for his attitude to the Grinnells and all privileged classes without freeing himself of his resentment and without understanding what it was in him that required the rebuke.

He looked around like a hunted creature, caught in the light of self-exposure. Everyone seemed to be having a good time as the music played, as feminine voices lightly trailed through the rooms. He was apparently the only one not drinking, not dancing, not enjoying himself. He shouldn't have come. He knew now, very clearly, *why* he had, but he should not have yielded to the temptation.

One or two of the local hostesses seemed available for either dancing or conversation but he held back. He was wary of small talk for one good reason: he might be enticed into forgetting Lois. The *mainstay*. More than ever his anchor. He would not jeopardize the relation for anything, even if it brought him temporary distraction from himself. Soon she would be visiting him again, staying at the same downtown boarding house after the long trip by the Fall River nightboat. Almost everyday she wrote him a letter, which had caused some stir in the Fort Rodman mailroom. Every day she brought him back to the best of their moments in Vermont and opened the door to an exciting life, sharing everything, going everywhere, conquering the world together!

But there was a problem, and there would likely be difficulty. She still did not truly know him as he was. In her high regard for his idealism she did not understand his materialistic drive, which this evening, in this very place, he was grasping in the clearest possible light.

Was he, in fact, a true materialist? Could there be any doubt? Deep within his emotive processes, beyond the level of rationalizing, he felt he was. If he were not, would he feel so self-conscious in the presence of the rich, so envying, so *hankering* for what they had, so dissatisfied with what he had—and *was*—himself?

What about his idealism, the dreams of service to mankind he had confessed to Lois? Yes, that was there too—both aspects were! Somehow both at the same time.

How to bridge the two, harmonize the discordances in his personality....

He glanced nervously around again, saw the other officers, some from the artillery, a few from other branches, enjoying themselves, drinking easily, refilling their glasses, having none of his conflicts.

Could taking a drink do something for him?....

He felt *gross:* not only from his heated, agitating trains of thought but from his country-bumpkin crudeness. *Bill Wilson, yokel.* He saw himself with uncomfortable clarity and did not like what he saw. He felt almost dehydrated with tension, with his unrelieved defensiveness. His mouth was dry, his tongue thick.

His mind, a tinderbox of urges and counter-urges.

He had finished the fruit drink and now stood hesitant, uncertain. A sudden tremor seized him. Just as he was beginning to panic—lest someone notice and *see* his distress—the trembling passed.

The room seemed full of another atmosphere just then, which he could not define. Something outside him, something within as well. There was in the air a sudden sense of strangeness ... as though he had inhabited another body.

Should he drink? Just one? What harm would there be in *that*? None really.

Even *if* he should, the worst that could happen would be a personal confirmation of all the warnings. In that event he would simply not drink again, but would have direct knowledge of the facts—would know *personally*.

On those grounds alone he ought to drink.

Why live his whole life and never really know what the truth here was? Was that a scientific approach to important questions? As things were now, it was really a superstition controlling him and not an established truth. The power of the *past*, dominating, shaping him, as it had in so many areas, making him no more than a pawn of other peoples' assumptions. Where was *freedom* in that?

He recalled that day in his early teens, which he had often thought about, when he went into the tavern with Mark Whalon ... recalled the coolness, the camaraderie, the *ease* he had felt, his congenial and comfortable mood, as opposed to the *dis*comfort he felt now. His father's world.

Ever since he had heard the warnings from his mother and his grandparents, for a full decade, he had rejected alcohol. But in so doing had he been symbolically rejecting his father too?

And then a vagrant, arresting thought: by drinking, would he absorb into himself the essence of his father's life and in effect create a private reconciliation between them?

"Not drinking, Lieutenant?" The female voice was siren-soft.

He turned. A pretty dark-eyed girl in a low-cut dress, resembling Lois, had appeared out of nowhere, standing close by with a drink in her hand which she held out to him. He had not seen her there before. She seemed to have materialized for his benefit, like a mermaid.

The crystal liquid in the cocktail glass glittered, sparkled, tantalized.

The warnings, the stories, all forgotten in an instant. He reached and took the glass. Or *someone* did. The personality spawned in his first twenty years—was it *him,* as he was—or...? *That* self, then, that identity, reached, stranger-like, unprompted, for the offered potion, the gleaming mysterious mixture.

He *sipped,* as he had seen others do, then sipped again, then again. Anyone watching would see that he was not overly impressed. But no one had noticed. And the mermaid had vanished back into her element—her task done.

Alone, yet not alone now, he stood there, very still, the drink partly consumed. A sensation like nothing he had ever experienced swept over him. More intense than anything known before. The effect made all the other moments of his life mild and fleeting.

There was a tingling in his toes, a warming in his stomach, a racing current in his blood, a dazzle of excitement in his brain.

Every fiber in his body palpitated with new life, throbbing with a vitality seemingly independent of him.

He finished the drink and looked around again, benignly, his face muscles relaxed, his mouth convolving in his eagerness to speak and sing. His arms and hands hung down in loose readiness to gesture freely, confidently.

He felt that he was projecting the very picture of youthful military leadership greatly enjoying his hours of relaxation away from the serious business of war training.

The drink had erased all barriers between himself and others. And it had done it at once, from the first contact with his tongue.

He thought expansively of the Grinnells, remembered that Emmy and Catherine Grinnell each had a man in the service, that Catherine had already lost hers in France. He tried to think of some way he could go up to them and ask their forgiveness, show his gratitude and admiration, express his hope to be able to partake of their gracious hospitality again soon.

He moved across the room to where the alcoholic beverages stood waiting. As deliberately as possible, while his hands trembled with eagerness and a sharp gloating cry coiled in his throat, he poured himself a mixture of vermouth and gin he had heard about, sipped it there, found it as potent as the first, then slowly, pacing his steps to appear entirely in control of himself, he began to move towards the others.

He felt utterly different to the person he had been only a few minutes before. He felt reborn, electrified, charged with what seemed limitless waves of energy and imagination.

The drink had given him a religious experience.

It had not created a false personality, it had uncovered the *true one,* revealed what was there to begin with: a smiling, life-loving, relaxed, all-embracing, self-confident, self-knowing individual in the prime of his youth capable of finding everyone interesting and everything relevant.

It had made him a true Number One man again!

This is how he would live henceforth ... *with this*! It wasn't after all a drug, but a social custom. Everybody drank.

But did everybody *feel this way*? If they did why hadn't he heard about it?

He doubted that they had. It would be *his* secret henceforth, his hidden weapon.

With *this* as his ally he would overcome any obstacle, attain any goal.

Wait until Lois heard the news! And the folks back home. He would inform them that not only did it not harm him but was the best thing that had ever happened to him.

He continued to sip steadily as he moved toward the other room, luxuriantly carpeted, where a group was gathered around the piano in one corner. He looked for the girl who had handed him the drink. He might dance with her. Which might make him forget his beloved Lois and perhaps put the wrong kind of ideas into his head. But she was nowhere to be seen. She seemed to have vanished into thin air. It was peculiar.

Just then he saw one of the Grinnell women coming down the stairs into the hall just outside the room where he stood. It was Catherine, or Katy as he had heard some of the officers call her, the one who had lost her husband in the trenches of France. A handsome, refined-looking, fair-haired, gracefully moving woman of about thirty in a dress of gleaming gold. The favorite of New Bedford society. Just the woman he wanted to see. Could he risk calling her Katy? He took another recharging swallow of his drink and, slightly beginning to sway, moved towards her, his face happy, smiling, his words ready to flow, ready to greet her as a sympathizing, understanding guest. At the bottom of the stairs she had stopped for a moment, looking around. It was as though she was waiting for someone to go up to her. A shower of benevolent thoughts poured through his mind....

She saw him coming. She beamed. "Lieutenant! How *winning* you look!"

Her voice, youthful and maternal at the same time, melted him. He held out his hand, confident, yet deferent. Softly his lips shaped her name. *Katy....*

Winning was how he felt.

PART TWO

8 The Ambiguities of Memory

As past and present fused, he both lived what he remembered and judged what he had done. Boundaries in consciousness blurred. Currents of time past swirled into the present and became part of his immediate knowing.

The magic of confessional memory: he was several parts of his being at the same time.

That scene at the Grinnells'—because of its truth, its fateful character—like yesterday. Everything prior had led up to it, everything afterwards away from it.

All the details recaptured ... except the drunkenness, then and later, being carried out by fellow officers, a matter of laughs to everybody. It was wartime, after all. Even Lois when she heard, untroubled. Besides, her thoughts were now preoccupied with wedding preparations—the date having been moved up to January 1918 in fear of his sudden departure for Europe.

As for his overindulgences: "Living with me, Bill, will be such an inspiration that you won't *think* of drinking!" He felt relieved, but deep down a shadow had fallen, silent and ominous.

Yes, at Grinnells'. Everything there that first time—the circle closed, the entity complete, the priming accomplished. Nothing later was added to the deadly mixture to make it—or *him*—more, or less, alcoholic. Nothing missing.

Nothing except its antidote, foreshadowed in two moments—transient, but too significant to overlook ... tentative precursors to the Towns awakening, *announcing* there was more to him than the record through New Bedford might suggest.

One occurred in England, while he was waiting in vain to become part of the war across the channel—a moment of truth enveloping him in Winchester Cathedral, whither he had wandered during a break in training routines: his emotional nature, from its exposure to weeks of anxious uncertainty, open to revelation. The secret power of Nature, an otherworldly grace, such as he had known more than once in Vermont, revisited him suddenly as he stood in the midst of the silent all-enclosing edifice, feeling some mystic presence around and within him, some charisma resident in the cathedral itself but equally taking its rise from silent cathedral depths within *him* and then projected into the surrounding space without. With the moment came also an abiding conviction of its truth, its sense of permanence, his certitude—borne out by time—that he would not forget, that though he did not understand it he knew beyond doubt that it would become part of him and in the unfolding design of his life play its role in ways he could not guess.

The other glimpse of something transcendental had taken place on the Rhode Island shore at Newport, earlier, in the summer, where he had been transferred to await shipment to England. Wandering to the edge of a great cliff overlooking the sea one warm and mysterious night, he and Lois together, just hours before his departure for Europe, had been caught up in the same spell as they stood hand in hand gazing at the moonlit sea.

Before the vastness of the great ocean stretching to the Old World neither had spoken, nor looked at the other, each filled with a separate burden of hope and fear and a sense of the eternal quality of the moment they were sharing.

Did searching the past bring enlightenment? Perhaps, after all, it did not. Or at best an uncertain truth. The main problem: in the lens of recollection the past was highly changeable. Psychiatry saw it as an objective *given,* perceptibly the same year by year, whereas in reality it was as volatile as the imagination of whoever probed it for analysis.

Memory was a fluctuating mirror that reflected back to you whatever you wanted.

Why then had he resurrected the past in his search for answers? Because of *yearning,* a homesickness for what *used to be.* Because of the nostalgic passion, the emotional urge—symbolically—to undo what had been *done,* in creative remembrance to live again in the dim halls of memory, to brood tirelessly over the lost years until in the crucible of imagination they had been remade nearer to the heart's desire. A craving every poet, every dreamer, every alcoholic knew.

No, the inconstant past which psychiatry explored, sounding out causes, was not what it seemed to be. We tried, for example, to avoid painful incidents in our formative years, yet these were the very experiences that charged us with potential for growth.

The larger picture glimpsed, what you might once have regretted became with time precious parts of the overall story: too valuable to be regretted. That they had *happened* was proof of their significance.

He was intrigued by the notion of opposite truths generated out of the emotional labyrinth of time. Whatever did not kill us would strengthen. Whatever comforted overmuch would weaken. Life built itself on this interaction of opposites changing their character in the cauldron of experiences actually being lived.

Winning, Katy Grinnell had said. But in winning, he had opened the door to enormous losing, in comparison to which death, over a period of nearly a decade, was no terror.

The moment that had given him the greatest single happiness up to then had made inevitable the horrors that followed, and yet those years of *losing* led in due course to Towns and Akron, the two victorious moments of his life.

And to AA.

So he could not regret anything that had happened.

Perhaps the root of this "good-out-of-evil, evil-out-of-good" syndrome lay in the allegory of the Fall ... though he was sure Dr. Bob would be bothered by his reference to anything in the Bible as allegorical. Had Adam not fallen he would have continued in his original state of all-contented nature, neither winning nor losing, neither growing nor declining, unaware of realities which, as he struggled out of the pit, he would eventually come to master.

The *fortunate* fall—which led, in the orthodox view, to Christ coming to the aid of stricken, sin-doomed humanity with the boon of salvation. Dr. Bob's view, and of the great majority of AA. Lois' view also. But not his. The allegorical interpretation ran deeper; it meant the Fall was constantly recurring—an *archetype,* as Carl Jung would have called it.

Chris Eastman's reading of St. Paul had been persuasive: Adam, after eons of laborious struggle, becomes the Christ. The real salvation, said Chris, was that Adam's new consciousness becomes that of Christ—an *achieved* salvation, not dependent upon the intercessory sacrifice of a man who may never have lived. It reflected the actual experiences of one's emotional life ... the area of truth in the total psyche.

"Adam would never have quested for God-consciousness," Chris had written to him in a letter, "if he had remained permanently in the Edenic state. In his fall, suffering, and banishment we have a legend of universal conflict, tragic heroism—and spiritual growth. There would have been no AA if your own childhood had been a paradise...."

If there was a Fall, and an Expulsion, then it was *his* fall, *his* expulsion, even as he rioted in the lethal glories of alcohol ... and ultimately his rise via sobriety to the great revelation.

In short, his decade-long hell of drunkenness, his purgatory of obsession, was the fortunate fall, the auspicious death-in-life, that led directly to AA. Therefore he embraced all the past, could not wish anything different than it had been.

Retracing the years to 1918 had taught him when and, to some extent, why he had become alcoholic, though that kind of knowledge, such as it was, could help him little. Psychiatry, mortgaged to the presumed wisdom of the past hidden in the subconscious, took that route, with its spectacularly poor results when treating alcoholics.

One might *develop* into an alcoholic, might pass through certain psychological stages to reach that point, but once arrived, one entered into a realm entirely different from the phases that had led to it. Becoming an alcoholic involved a state transcending causation ... an *elemental* condition.

Once manifested, it could not be reversed by merely psychological methods, which belonged to a more empirical domain. Only another element equally strong and primal could displace it.

Like the AA program.

Like spiritual awakening.

One *power* standing off another, neutralizing it. One obsession fighting another. Alcoholism, essentially a *state,* capable perhaps of being described by the intellect but in essence beyond the intellect's comprehension.

The intellect did not deal with *states of being,* only with their manifestations, which were no more like the reality than a visible tumor like the inner experience of cancer, or the outward signs of frailty and uncertainty like the experience of growing old.

The substance of it was that with alcoholism you experienced a condition of *being,* whereas in searching the past you dealt with *categories,* symptoms, *relative things...*

Still one hoped, one pursued the act of memory, despite its ambiguities, rewarded by the occasional flash of understanding and self-discovery.

And powered by the desire to possess all that life, that lived history, those haunting, vanished times ... embracing the past with its shadows and mutability—nurturing, cherishing it, refusing to let it fall under the sway of oblivion altogether.

9 A Wedding and Its Aftermath

Before the limbo years began in 1919, the disjointed dream, there was his marriage in January 1918 and its immediate aftermath, a short period in which the effect of the first drunkenness and frequent recurrences had not yet recast his mind in a new image, when he was still recognizable as the personality he had been.

He was, in fact, already alcoholic but the obsession had not yet infiltrated all the ramparts of consciousness. He was for a while longer, less than a year at most, enjoying—though in diminishing degrees—the sense of freedom of choice. Perhaps he had already lost that power but the change was so new that he had the illusion of being someone who could or could not take a drink as it pleased him.

In fact, it was pleasing him all the time to do so, but he could, on special occasions, though these were few, abstain totally. He had already begun, in other words, to be guided by fear, sensing that he could control the problem only by remaining dry, that somehow the first taste of the alcohol, even the *prospect* of the first taste, was enough to make him quite irrational, instinct-dominated, changing from one instant to another with lightning swiftness.

If he could remain dry he could at least outwardly resemble the person others expected him to be, but going *without* left him in a state of dissatisfaction and uneasiness, with always the undercurrent of fear. Left him feeling *strange* ... knowing all the while what would quickly enough remedy that condition.

The wedding was one such special occasion, his abstinence ironically conspicuous in the midst of the post-nuptial celebration. His habitual constraint with the Burnhams—for all their genuine fondness for him and the pains they took to make him comfortable in their world—with the excitement of the wedding to augment his tension, made the thought of alcohol especially attractive and his unbroken control a matter of some astonishment to himself ... leading him to believe that his iron will was potent proof, if any was needed, that there *was* no drinking problem.

Nevertheless something connected with his newly experienced fear, surging suddenly to life over the past month, or since that day in New Bedford, compelled him to deny himself the dangerous pleasure of the first drink: he was confronted by the unexpected news that neither his mother nor sister would be in attendance at the ceremony, due to an illness which, he was told, had struck them both at the same time on the eve of the wedding.

As he pondered the matter, he was not surprised at his mother's absence. He remembered her telling him, that day in her Arlington office, that often people became ill when they wished. Now it was her turn.

But why would she choose to absent herself from such an event as her son's wedding ... unless in her heart she disapproved of it—not of Lois, for she had met her during one of her trips from Boston to East Dorset and, as with everybody else, had liked her immediately. It was rather the fact that her ineffectual progeny was actually getting married was itself something she found difficult, perhaps intolerable, to accept.

Her image of him, he well knew, was of an inadequate emotional *male*—of the same gender as the man who had mistreated her long ago—who would never be able to properly fill his place in the world, someone of whom she would never really be proud. All his failures and illnesses seemed to confirm her estimate. Marriage, on the other hand, meant an acceptance of responsibility, an alliance with values beyond himself—not to speak of his notable success in soldiering ... developments that gave the lie to her image of him, that indicated the son *she* knew was a figure of the past, perhaps of her imagination.

Ideas that offended her. Whatever the evidence might be of a *new* Will, she would not accept the change, preferring the conception that fed her own life-attitudes toward the whole male sex.

In her mind she continued to relate to him as he had been at Burr and Burton and at Norwich, and *that* son could not be seen as compatible with the notion of marriage, particularly to so balanced, mature, and clear-seeing a young woman as Lois Burnham obviously was.

And perhaps, as well, the whole idea of *marriage* itself—that hated condition in her memory—brought back with painful symbolic directness the bitter, unhappy time of her life. Did she dare trust herself to keep her composure in the church while the ceremony progressed? Might she have feared some uncontrollable outburst for which she would never forgive herself ... or forgive *him,* also?

The drama of the wedding, and his being the only Wilson or Griffith among so many Burnhams, distracted him effectively from this train of thought or even of dwelling upon the fact of his mother's absence. It was only as evening approached and he and Lois made their plans for a hurried departure for their New Bedford apartment retreat that he found himself once again prey to these ruminations.

They had originally planned to take the train to Fall River and thence the boat to New Bedford—Lois' route on so many occasions. But now it was decided between them that after telephoning his mother and Dorothy they would take the night train to Boston's South Station and then by bus head out to Arlington. In the afternoon they could conveniently connect with a local train going to New Bedford south of Boston.

He could not recall for sure whether it was he or Lois who first made this suggestion. Lois always claimed it was she, declaring "I was the one who brought Bill and his mother together"—which he was willing to let stand. It had pleased him that she had seemed proud of her contribution to the shaping of her husband in a mold of heroic manhood. But in fact, once he found a moment's freedom upstairs, apart from the wedding party in the downstairs rooms at Clinton Street, he had felt it *necessary* to see his mother while the wedding was still a matter of urgency and before they returned to the wartime atmosphere of New Bedford and his looming duties at Fort Rodman.

He *had* to see her just then. Whatever *her* attitude might be. He was doing it for his own sake, for self-preservation, as much as from filial duty, convinced as before that he could not afford to have his mother—or his father—recede from an important role in his life.

It was likely neither he nor Lois who had initiated the call to Arlington, but simply the reality of the situation revealing itself and determining the course they had to follow if his mother's failure was not to be left unredeemed.

But there was something else. There was a struggle for moral superiority in the conflict between him and his mother. The idea was disconcerting, but it was perhaps the chief strain in their relationship, made all the more evident by her self-description as a person of righteous morals who never had hesitated to lecture others on their duties and obligations, doing so with special emphasis where he—the unworthy son—was concerned. In pushing himself on her just now, in visibly refusing to allow himself to resent her nonappearance at his wedding, coming to her in his officer's uniform and a splendid new wife on his arm, he was *forcing* her to react, demonstrating his *superior* morality and sense of what was right in parenting *her* ... as he had done four years ago when, though with far different emotional components involved, he had made the journey to Marblehead.

Looking back, he was certain this factor had been there from the beginning—with both parents, though principally of course with his mother. Had he known it at the time? Probably not in a conscious sense but instinctively he had felt its driving undercurrent—a duel, in a final analysis, of *egos*.

He was relieved that it was Dorothy, now nineteen, who answered the phone, her enthusiasm for their plan unmistakable. She spoke rapidly before their mother could take the phone from her.

"You're right to come, Will! It will be wonderful to see you. I was so *sorry* we weren't there, but I was thinking of you every moment.... Yes, you must come! It's wartime, after all. Who knows what will happen tomorrow? People have to *act,* to *do* things—or forever regret not doing them!"

She had expressed his own feelings precisely and Lois' too, making him feel proud of her.

His mother demurred about the visit, declaring she was still not feeling well, though he noted that both she and Dorothy had never sounded more normal. But in view of the fact that the three young people wanted the meeting she had to comply, unable, he was aware, to generate more than a minimal encouragement for the reunion.

What he remembered about the long trip by night train to Boston was that he and Lois huddled close to each other in the cramped seats and while they slept they were filled with a romantic sense of being alone in the world.

The fact of their marriage against the presumed threat of wartime separation at any hour gave them a feeling of joy and achievement, overriding what otherwise would have been the tremors of anxiety as they approached the South Station and then proceeded by subway and bus to Arlington. The voices of life sang so triumphantly in their hearts that the life-denying compulsions of his mother were rendered of little effect.

In this mood he felt he could handle alcohol, which he had successfully denied himself during the day of the wedding, but none was readily available and he felt it would be awkward to suggest to Lois that they go out of their way to obtain some. She read his thoughts: "When we reach New Bedford we'll both make up for it!"

Upon their arrival, his mother used the excuse of a contagious cold, a clearly nonexistent one, to avoid embracing him. He felt sorry for the limitations she had imposed upon herself, felt sorry for his father, for himself, and for Dorothy doing her best to grow into normal young womanhood in the presence of something so undesirable in their mother.

Her hostility to alcohol in any form was well known in the family, hence there was no problem of abstaining from a drink during their visit. But in his mind's depths the explosive ingredients for a bout of intoxication, the moment alcohol was available, had collected.

Instead tea was served, with little cakes, and sandwiches on white bread, which he devoured in lieu of affection from his mother. He and Lois after departing the night train in Boston had enjoyed a full breakfast of eggs and coffee at one of the indoor arcades in the South Station, but that seemed hours ago. He ate as informally as he used to do in East Dorset, perhaps to reassure his mother and sister that the Army had changed him only superficially.

They talked of the war, of activity at Fort Rodman, with particular reference to all the rumors that his artillery unit would soon be shipped overseas, and the three women inspected him with measuring pathos, wondering if Will, suddenly more heroic-looking, might be one of those never to come back. Were his mother's eyes glistening with repressed sorrow?

Dorothy put her latest record of war songs on the Victrola and they listened with quiet excitement. "Over There," "Goodbye Broadway, Hello France," "It's a Grand Old Flag."

Her voice taut, her eyes aglow, Lois then exclaimed: "When Bill was adjutant for the day at Rodman you should have seen him on the parade ground commanding his men in drill formations, striding out in front so manly and assured to the strains of 'Stars and Stripes Forever'. It was, let me tell you both, most thrilling to see!"

Whereupon Dorothy picked out another record, wound the Victrola again, and played them Sousa's march, which they listened to emotionally, the three women—his mother included—gazing at the soldier with pride and satisfaction. He swelled with pride himself and felt gratitude to Lois and Dorothy for their inspirations.

Nothing further was said about the troublesome colds or the wedding, everyone united in a mutually shared agreement to pass the subject over in silence.

The visit was short—tacitly that was their intention. But he was glad they had come, sure they had done the right thing, believing he had won another round in the battle of wills with his mother—wishing he did not have to.

Glancing at Lois while they were still in the apartment, he saw that she seemed to have read the substance of his thoughts ... though she could not have guessed their emotional coda in a burst of keenly contemplated alcoholic relief.

Gradually there was a slow, steady movement toward the door, as he and Lois retrieved their winter coats. Dorothy seized his hand and kissed him on the cheek warmly. "Take care of yourself, Lieutenant!"

At the same time his mother gave him a quick, cordial embrace, scarcely felt through his military greatcoat but worth the visit.

There was a general exchange of pleasantries hurriedly delivered as the wind outside blew over the cobblestones.

"I'm glad you came, Will!" his mother exclaimed suddenly, as though unable to conceal her true sentiments any longer.

Proof that Lois had not read all his thoughts came later in pouring them a glass of wine to celebrate what they had been through in the past twenty-four hours. The gesture was innocent, as though she had never heard of his sorry record at the post and in later New Bedford forays, even in the last month. It was as though she was trying, by her visible faith in his ability to drink intelligently, to banish the problem and condition him to reflect in his actions the same faith.

The plan, if that was what it was, did not succeed. If ever anyone had an excuse, he thought, to drink to his heart's content, it was he; and that he did—to drunkenness and passing out in the armchair before midnight, giving her, the day after their wedding, her first experience in undressing him and throwing a blanket over his crumpled sleeping form.

Opening his mail the next day, he found, among a number of congratulatory wedding messages, a letter forwarded by Grandmother Wilson—from Gilman, announcing his intention soon to visit New Bedford, spend some time again with his son, and meet the girl he had married.

On an impulse he went outside, stretched comfortably in the benign ambient summer leafage of approaching dusk, breathed in the heady mix of flowering odors of greenery and earth, reflected that he had taken no exercise today but lacked interest in doing so now— though just before he went to bed he might take a stroll in the cooler night air....

Was he hungry enough yet for an early meal in Lois' absence? He decided he was and, suiting action to thought, began moving toward the house over the gentle slope of their secluded property. He walked with deliberation, with a deceptively serene carriage, as though taking responsibility for the past, for all he had lived through—and indeed, he thought, ultimately one had to do that. Nothing could really happen to you by chance, both the things you did and the things that you drew *to* you—everything must be seen, in time, as part of destiny.

With these thoughts filling his mind he moved with quiet consciousness of the past, and its presences, its soundless voices, its dissolving faces moved with him—a train of images accompanying him as he headed for the back door of the house, his usual entrance at times like this.

The aloneness soothed him, surrounded him with enveloping peace, or what seemed to be peace. It was a priceless gift. His long companionship with Lois had saved him but at times, as now, he wondered if he was cheating himself of the nourishment of sufficient solitude, even with the studio available. And yet to be *alone* in his present condition would beyond question be a fearsome prospect—and a possible prelude to drinking again.

No, the combination he had was the best for him—for Lois too. He must not quarrel with his great good fortune in having found the one woman meant truly for him.

He entered the kitchen, put the meat loaf on the table while preheating the oven, and stood pondering his own thoughts for some time, the sounds and sights of his memory for the moment wrapped up in Lois, so central a part of his past....

When his father had arrived at the New Bedford train station in March of 1918, leaving behind his second wife Christine and his new daughter, Helen, he declared, with gruff good-humor but mixed with a measure of serious intent, that he had come chiefly to meet the girl his son had married and that he intended to spend more time with her than with him, which in fact is what happened. And through it all Lois had been a model of warm hospitality, exhibiting a genuine pleasure towards her father-in-law and a tireless interest in the anecdotes and opinions he poured out to her.

They had taken to each other with an almost immediate attraction, though he realized that their swift mutual acceptance was something in which they both had a strong vested interest.

While the loaf was reheating in the oven, he moved into the spacious old-fashioned living room with the outsize stone fireplace dominating, seated himself in his favorite rocker after taking down from the wall his well-worn violin. Absently he plucked on the strings and watched more intently the movement of his thoughts across the stages of the past.

His father's visit had come in the midst of intensive preparations his battery was making to depart for a post near Newport, the site from which they would, at some still unannounced date, disembark for overseas. As a result, father and son saw much less of each other during his week in New Bedford than he would have liked ... though from the little they actually had to say necessity had proved to be a benevolent mother. The discovery was vaguely distressing, but all too true.

Having Lois available was a godsend for both. Had she not been, the mutual embarrassment would have been unendurable. He would have ended by breaking his vow of not drinking while Gilman was there.

At such times his urge to drink sprang not from a compulsion to escape some mood or frustration closing in on him, such as he had experienced at the Grinnells' that first time, but to heighten the feeling of reconciliation that affected both father and son.

His father, in fact, drank a good deal of beer and ale during that week and with Lois a fair amount of wine; he himself had been present on these occasions perhaps half the time, somewhat ostentatiously nursing cups of tea or coffee, envying both his father and his wife their alcoholic control. It was obvious that Gilman was no problem drinker, only a man who had found in regular drinking, mostly ale, an escape from a life of hard work.

"We were never suited, Will," he confessed one night while Lois had left to do some shopping in the town. "Never should have married. I don't blame her for what she did. We made each other miserable. It would have only gotten worse...."

His father's second marriage had clearly brought him not only happiness but an equanimity and acceptance toward what had happened long ago that was reassuring to see.

"... And I give her due credit," Gilman went on, "for seeing you got into Norwich Academy. At the time it mightn't have seemed what you wanted, but with us being in the war and all, it turned out to be a ten-strike. Look at you now—you're in the driver's seat. A second lieutenant—on your way up, from what Lois has been telling me!" He reached for the glass of ale, his motion, like his voice and facial expression, expansive, calm, pleased with himself. "... Yes, I give her credit, full credit."

He knew it was the ale speaking but it was Gilman too that spoke. Again he felt a strong urge to join him in this rare mood of forgiveness and magnanimity. A glass of ale did not seem like much. In his hesitation he was on the verge of breaking his resolution but he feared jeopardizing his father's visit, the auspicious harmony that had developed between Gilman and Lois, and his reputation as a promising young officer of the United States Army.

Feared for them. Feared for himself ... feared what, in the guise of alcoholic joy, had dawned in his soul.

The visit ended. Both he and his father, as well as Lois, were satisfied it had come to pass. He reflected that the Marblehead trip of four years ago had made it possible for him and Gilman to have occasional contact henceforth, perhaps in widely spaced parts of the continent. And the January meeting with his mother and Dorothy had kept open the lines of communication there. Those were the key encounters for all of them.

From New Bedford, Gilman, while still in the East, would travel to Vermont to visit his mother, the two elder Griffiths (for whom he retained affectionate sentiments), and former friends and coworkers still active around the old Dorset Quarry.

His son next month would entrain for Newport and then leave for England, where he and his battery, superbly trained by then, with mixed emotions sat out the war ... the strange mystic moment in Winchester Cathedral his only dramatic experience: wherein he had rediscovered the other half of his being. One half (masked as liberation) would evoke fear; the other, awe. His soul would be their battleground.

The conflict in France was over before he could join in. The great war had not needed him.

He would have to seek glory on other fields.

10   The Dark Presence

After finishing his meal he returned for a time to the rocker near the fireplace and idly picked up the violin again, randomly drawing the bow across the strings, evoking nostalgic harmonies, but unable to maintain interest now in sense phenomena, even those of his beloved music, which had so often assuaged him.

Another music drew him, the music of time—and of his own mind, somber though it might be.

At length he stood up, left on the lights in kitchen and living room to create an image of occupancy for unwanted eyes, as well as to give Lois upon her return the comforting look of a lighted home, and started back to the studio just beyond the knoll in the distance, a two-minute walk away. *His* place, his den, his cave of quiet. He felt as though reconnecting with a part of his life no one knew of—not even Lois or Chris: his truly secret hours. With all their mysteries.

Seated again at his writing desk in the familiar swivel-chair, he felt more comfortable, his journal near at hand if he should need it.

Without difficulty he recaptured his last train of thought...

Glory? Had he found it?

Such as few had experienced. Perhaps such as no one had, except the founders of religions and spiritual movements, mystics, prophets. The *adulation*—unique to such people, and to himself!

How *odd* that it should happen to *him,* that *he* should be linked with such a charismatic group? *Him* ... agnostic, critic of religion, skeptic, Nature-worshipper at best ... despite his friendship with Reverend Sam and Father Ed and his one-to-one seminars with Fulton Sheen! Down deep he was something they could not have guessed—only another alcoholic, who by definition would, at least during his active days, be agnostic too.

In fact, as he saw more and more clearly, religion had nothing to do with what had happened to him at Towns—Chris Eastman's oft-repeated argument. Religion was man-made, church-bred. Spiritual experience, as he had directly perceived, was something else altogether: a near-unbeliever being plunged directly into the heart of that mystical intuition which, as Chris had told him, was the ground of true religion.

Still, that the acclaim had fallen on *him* was something he could never grasp. He may have wanted to be number one, but *this* was taking that concept and turning it into a power of enormous magnitude! All the while, in the unavailing gloom, knowing only too well his unworthiness of the accolade.

Glory, yes—unchosen glory.

Baffled and vexed once more, feeling *hounded,* as he always did when this subject arose ever since the flight from Los Angeles. Anxiously, with an effort of will, he tried to return his mind to its tour of the past, and after a few uneasy minutes succeeded.

1919.

The very sound of that year was like an overture, dividing his world.

The beginning of the fifteen years' dream, the decade and a half which even as he lived through it seemed unreal—the whole period merely a rough draft of an existence.

Before 1919 he had known a self, a center emerging in accordance for the most part with familiar patterns. His ego had been involved of course but not uniquely so. At least it was controlled, subordinated to the *birth of an identity.*

After 1919 there was no real center developing, only *alcoholism* and its twin presence, *ego,* which, once the door was opened, now flourished rankly, like a poisonous, insatiable nightweed.

That was one of his major discoveries during his journey into the
past: that it wasn't so much his alcoholism that had spread like a cancer
during those years but the ego that had powered it. For the ego was
still with him, more inflamed—if covertly so—than in the twenties,
before it had begun its career pervading every avenue of his life. It had
camped possessively at his door, a tenacious guest, pressing him close
in a tight embrace.

His life throughout those fifteen years—coincident, as he so often
reflected, with the span of Prohibition—could have been lived in an
entirely other way and there would have been no special difference.
Dominated by the specter of addiction, almost all his actions—
increasingly, progressively—were rendered trivial, grotesque, unbalanced.

Nothing he did was of any significance. Even by 1919 he was
alcoholic—hence all his projects thereafter radically flawed at the
outset: he may not have been drinking at any particular occasion but
at *all* times his mind was steeped in the alcoholic psychology.

The overriding motif of the whole period was his living an *obsessed*
life—and in secret. Various projects that emerged were but footnotes
to the main text: his alcoholism and the emotional nature that gradually
fell under its sway. When plans succeeded he toasted himself in victory,
when they failed he wallowed in self-pity and drank to soothe his
wounded ego. Drinking and the dreams it engendered had become
the one truly important business of his life.

Everything was shadowed and undercut by the sense of unreality
that haunted him—by the vice draining him year by year of his
manhood and the meaning of his existence. Always in the back of his
mind he thought that when the duty was performed, the act disposed
of, the meeting adjourned, or *whatever* the occasion, he could soon
begin the serious part of the day—drinking.

Always the rationalization that it made him feel *better,* a new man,
free of frustrations at not being able to find a job, at no longer being
accorded the automatic respect that went with a lieutenant's bar, free
of anxieties over just what he was supposed to do with his life (without
training for anything in particular), free of resentments over what he
still felt were the superior ways the Burnhams instinctively adopted
towards him (the good-natured, not-too-well-educated country boy

admired because of what *Lois* saw in him), and free of upwelling moods of inadequacy that like a creeping sickness overspread the country of his mind, and left him feeling that some unavoidable *doom* was his personal fate, that a condign and oppressive script had already been written beyond his power to influence it—only to endure it.

More effectively endured with the help of alcohol.

And this doom-bent state the result, he had no doubt, *of his own character*—his rooted feeling of ever standing apart from others, from Life, from the deep truth of things, whatever that might be. *That*—that conviction, that habitual mindset—was beyond question the thing that drove him to drink and from which in alcohol he sought refuge in a less anxious, less ominous personality.

Drinking to escape the self he was and awaken the self he could be, the serene and ever-affirming self that came to him like a magic genie in the bottle, and in fact able to make contact with this power readily, particularly in the early twenties and during the initial stages of any given round of drinking, when his senses and brain were fresh and the serpentine grip of the alcohol had advanced only moderately through the tissues of his psyche.

That was the early charming stage when he was attractive and convincing to everyone, including Lois, who at such times—remaining thoroughly unaware of the seething mind behind his still-graceful alcoholic gestures—was almost able to tease him about his weakness, jokingly concerned about his vaunted willpower, and he answering that his willpower was not in evidence because he saw no need for it... the stage when his personality under the influence, still benign, of the drink, was almost always *winning*, as Katy Grinnell had exclaimed that day.

This was the stage when the true joy of drinking was so well known to every alcoholic, for whose transformative powers they returned to the contest over and over, no matter how many times they failed, no matter that *every* time—even in the heady early periods—they did fail, did end up in trouble or drunk or disgraced in any one of innumerable ways!

He had talked of this glowing, auspicious early stage with many sober members of AA, and with none more pointedly than with Chris, who declared: "It had to be a mystical experience we were seeking, as William James implied, and which to some extent we attained, at least for short intense periods—when we reigned triumphant!"

He could not quarrel with that; it accorded with his own experience.

The search for mystical experience through alcohol! The drive for self-transcendence through the ecstasy of drink!

Many in AA, like Dr. Bob, downplayed the whole idea, to be sure: dismayed to hear mysticism and plain hard-drinking alcoholism linked together. To them it seemed pretentious and vaguely profane. A mixing of the sublime with the worldly in an incomprehensible manner.

But those who held that belief, he could have added, would have difficulty with their drinking problem. As Bob always had from the first, almost every day contending with the recurrent desire, hardly ever knowing the spiritual uplift of the AA potential, its encouragement to a regenerate experience for any member who followed the Twelve Step program, a life in which the threat of drinking, absorbed into the new consciousness, would gradually—in some cases, like himself and Chris Eastman, almost overnight—vanish, practically never to return.

Yes, truly liberated, freed, new-born ... attaining a state, as Chris had denominated it, Beyond Sobriety.

So he had heard, so written, so declared from many a rostrum.

Managing to escape the benefits by discovering the world of his cave.

True, no drinking again, the desire evaporated. But something "beyond sobriety"? The equivalent on a day-by-day basis of the Towns revelation? No, nothing like that. Instead....

What he now had, what he now was.

His thoughts grew clouded, swirled upon themselves. With an effort he restored the thread of his attention....

The *glow,* leading to ecstasy and moments of fulfillment that seemed to make it all worthwhile....

But then discovering it took longer each week to attain that state, and the reaction afterwards—longer and more vexatious each time.

At which point it became drinking not to escape *into* something but *away* from something, the consciousness he had fallen into after the now increasingly short-lived euphoria—that sensation of mystical oneness to which James had referred in his *Varieties of Religious Experience* and which Chris emphasized in their talks—that *all-winning* fascination that earlier, and rashly, he had identified with the ritual act of drinking itself.

The dark side of life, the *adversary principle,* was evoked in the negative aftermath of the early bonhomie. Elements of both good and evil were tapped, both poles of human nature, but over time the latter especially, for if the good was dominant in addictive drinking it would legitimize alcoholism itself.

Did the alcoholism *cause* the dark element?

Rather, the darkness *manifested* as the alcoholism—and as the obsessive, driven, *captured* life that followed.

Was it permanent, then—this element of darkness?

He hesitated, pausing almost tangibly in his thought-grapplings....

Yes, as long as it was needed it was permanent, which meant that it was intrinsic in almost everyone's life, not alcoholics alone. In the divine economy of existence the darkness and its other forms—ego, chiefly—was an essential feature. Ego—that is, this struggle *against* it, and the mysterious zone of darkness out of which it appeared—provided the means to develop will! *To the making of a soul.*

It was not only Chris and the mystics who knew these things. He also, from the depths of his inertia and will-less darkness, embosomed in the clutch of the adversary, *knew.* He had been preoccupied with them for so long that it would be strange if he *didn't.*

His mind reverted to the notion of the fortunate fall for confirmation of this idea—the concept of everything being useful and needed.

Only through evil could a true good emerge. As he could demonstrate convincingly enough from his own case.

Then another thought came, which he had shared with Chris. When the purpose *was* achieved, when the will *was* developed, the soul realized *finally*—what then? Did this dark power go on existing? Chris said that it would vanish in the transforming fire of mystical *knowing,* the experience that made the saint, which, he added, was the will of God. "*This* is the will of God," he had declared, quoting St. Paul, "namely, your sanctification."

Not merely "improving our conscious contact with the divine," as the Eleventh Step had it. Far more: sanctification, perfection, oneness with the Supreme. Was it possible? All the world's scriptures affirmed that it was.

No more need of will *then*—one moved into the garment of the new Self, freed permanently, then, of the contraries, the struggle in the breast between the two forces. After the ego, the adversary, the diabolic presence—having served a unique saving purpose—was no more.

Meanwhile he lay enmeshed in the fetters of the struggle, the clash of the contraries, someone for whom the ego was—and had been for these five years past—*more real than the deity.*

It was to escape this darkness—appearing first as frustration, jealousy, resentment, fear, self-pity—that he drank in the first place. The darkness did not begin *as such*—it began as conflict, anxiety, bitterness, feelings of guilt and inadequacy, and the like. Only *later* was its true character revealed.

Not its *alcoholic* character. Its character per se.

The darkness principle, he was convinced, was, equally with the spiritual, a rooted and universal reality in *human* nature, not in addicts alone. Alcoholics had merely been forced to wrestle with this unleashed power, usually to their ruin, for it was a destructive energy, ultimately invincible when freed from the usual controls.

He was also convinced—though again it was not something he had ever raised publicly, in fact not to anyone at all except to Chris on one occasion—that it was this specter-like ego, this gorge of craving in every heart, this devouring force of self unmitigated, *and not the alcohol,* that destroyed the individual ... taking the *form* of alcoholism to gain dominance over the individual life.

Again, so long as they remained in ignorance of the true nature of their problem alcoholics were among the most unfortunate of souls, for this dark hell-power had open access to their lives, and every moment, whether sober or drunk, was killing them *without their knowledge* ... when they gained understanding, as in AA, they were among the most fortunate for now they had the opportunity to gain dominance over *it*, particularly if they opened themselves to the grace of spiritual energies available to them.

And could he not do that, help himself—as once he had—against the same destructive force? Could he not renew once again the AA program—his own creation—*for himself* and recharge his life with new power and incentive?

His thinking circled to a halt as he pondered an answer. There *was* no good reason why not, why he continued to *allow* the depression to rule him so one-sidedly. He had liberated himself once, knew the way to do so again ... except that now the ego was fighting for its life, the darkness had usurped so much influence these past five years that in attempting to do now what he had done most notably in 1934 and 1935 at Towns and Akron he would be contending with a reality much more formidable than earlier, a reality—a negative self—he had strengthened by having identified with it—on both conscious and unconscious levels—for so long.

He could do it. But the will, the energy *to* do it—had he lost contact with that potential? It almost seemed that he had.

More specifically, there was the challenge Chris Eastman had posed almost from the beginning of their friendship four years ago....

11 The Spiritual Challenge

Was Chris right? Was AA only the beginning? Was he meant to found ... *a new religion*? That is what Gerald Heard and to some extent the Princess had urged upon him, too ... providing he began with a change in himself first of all.

Or even, to keep it simpler: in turning away from the path Chris had strongly recommended—the way of *mysticism*—was he denying himself the secret object behind his drinking, perhaps the goal of his entire life?

The mystic way had succeeded with Chris, there was no doubt of that. When they had talked of the psychology of drinking, of the successive stages in an evening or in a career of addictive indulgence, it was clear that Chris had all but forgotten the phenomenon of the "glow" for one very good reason: although reluctant to speak of it, he had experienced the real thing. More than once. The enduring presence of the True had blotted out the recollection of the Painted True, the False True.

He had known an ecstasy that had not ended in bitterness.

Could he not, himself, make a decision to direct his own life toward that higher state as well, beyond—yes, much beyond—even what he had experienced at Towns fifteen years ago? At least there was no doubt that he *should*.

The memory of *how* he had drunk, was itself enlightening: *violently,* in a spirit of consuming desire to exhaust the transformations hidden in the alcohol, compelled to *oppose* something there, as swiftly as possible to enter another consciousness ... obviously someone looking for an immediate answer to his personality lacks, to his personality itself, craving balance, joy, power, unlimited confidence and well-being where, down deep, there was unreality.

Meditation, not merely as an adjunct to prayer, a simple and vague kind of outreach toward the idea of the deity, but as a finely honed, sophisticated discipline with its roots in Eastern yoga, at least as Chris spoke of it—that kind of meditation, in view of his own past history, seemed called for.

Meditation, the mystic path, a commitment to the higher life— just as, in alcoholic terms, commitment to the life AA offered the still suffering drinker—was his passport to a transformed consciousness.

That seemed appropriate now.

But the very thought raised up in him a sudden and instant opposition, an almost desperate protest from some buried center within his psyche.

He paused, thought a moment, came to a conclusion.

Not a *spiritual* center perhaps. More likely the ego's lair stirred to revolt, sowing seeds of confusion in his mind, and succeeding all too well.

Telling him: he was no mystic, no saint! At the age of fifty-three, for one thing, he was too old to begin.

Chris had conceded that "younger was better" but that fifty-three was not *too* old, that there was still time, particularly in view of his background in reading, and his guidance of others within AA for the past fourteen years. There were cases, he said, of people who had begun at fifty-three or even older and had achieved regeneration.

But how many offhand could he cite? *Not many.*

No, his character was formed by now. For five years past it was no character to be proud of; but there, for good or ill, it was.

Nevertheless, even as, once again, he made up his mind upon this subject, he had opened the locked drawer in his desk, where he kept his journal, and took out Chris' long letter, arrived two weeks ago, and reread the main paragraphs:

> ... Emerson's remark that an institution is the lengthened shadow of one man is borne out by AA singularly. The whole fellowship has taken its cue and character from what you, its founder, have given to it. And that has been a marvelous legacy. Your ideas have become ours, your ideal of sobriety ours, your basic understanding of the alcoholic problem— which has been so searching—ours also. The influential literature of AA has been what *you* have written. Almost no organization that I can think of—except a few that have been developed frankly as religions—has so reflected the viewpoint of a single individual. And that, despite the obvious risks potentially involved, has proved a blessing for everyone.

> But it seems to me the time has come—and that time I believe is overdue—for you to enlarge your vision of what it means to be a recovered alcoholic, so that countless others—even only hundreds of others, if it came to that—would be motivated to expand their own horizons and reach out to a

fuller and more appropriate destiny, fulfilling ourselves as the *souls* that we are.

You yourself have said in the Big Book that the hidden purpose of AA is to bring its members to God. The degree of God-knowledge most of us have so far attained in AA is minimal indeed, but with your example provided here, as it has been in so many other areas from the beginning, a great opportunity awaits us. I believe you are called now to realize your true potentialities as a Moses of *this* people—this unique following that you have, growing by tens and soon hundreds of thousands each year—by leading them to a new conception of life and humanity, with AA as it is presently constituted as the foundation for a genuine call to arms, an invitation to recognize itself as the latest authentic religion mankind has developed—a religion of potential saints drawn exclusively from acknowledged sinners.

But unless you lead us—who *else* can do so?—this grand promise, bursting to be realized, will remain only an idea in the heads of a few people.

I am not alone in thus urging you to revitalize AA—if necessary, to create a new movement consisting of those willing and ready to follow you—to renew AA by first renewing yourself...

Then he had indicated ways he could introduce him to friends he had met in Manhattan—swamis, mystics—who would facilitate the passage from where he stood now to where he might be in a year or two—and of course how AA would be affected if he accepted the challenge and the intensive practice of meditation as the way to make the mystic path meaningful.

But for such a conversion to be valid you had to want it yourself with all your heart and soul. *He did not feel that way,* and there was no way he was going to manufacture the requisite attitude.

How in his present Slough could he take such a step—how *enact* it, how *grasp* the reality of another spiritual milieu so utterly different from the dark and drifting, powerless world in which he secretly dwelled? How generate the will?

Inertia, triumphant for so many months, had all but immobilized him.

And even if he *could* make the effort, will himself into a state suitable for such a turning, would it simply be *ego at work again*?

Bill W., Mystic, Sage!

Blithely ignoring the rank and file membership of AA, for whom the gift of sobriety had been their all-in-all?

Lois had known the letter from Chris had come but he had kept its contents from her; she would have been dismayed by what she read—in this and some of the other messages Chris sent him: of late adopting the epistolary mode of communication fairly often. He himself had felt inhibited by what his younger friend wrote. He could guess how it would have been for her.

Alcoholism and the AA solution, despite her elation and relief at what had happened to her husband, had mystified her, and now Chris Eastman's ideas—particularly from what she could gather of their *mystical* content—had troubled her still more. He knew how uneasy she was confronting these *outré* ranges of experience. Strong, faithful, intelligent as she was, Lois did not have the character type for mystical revelation—as Dr. Bob did not, and—he had no doubt—as the great majority of AAs did not. She was a hands-on, practical, self-confident woman lacking, when all was said and done, the karmic development to be sympathetic to mysticism. She, like Bob and the vast majority out there, was a capable, *once-born* soul. That was the key, the problem, and the mystery. It was inevitable she would have been uncomfortable with Chris, who, as a result, almost never visited him at the house.

"He's not a real AA member in my view, Bill!"

Because there was some truth in her remark, he had said nothing, though he wished she had not spoken.

"He talks about meditating but we have been meditating ever since your Towns experience and I have been doing it all my life."

He pointed out that Chris saw it as a special discipline to be mastered after a fairly long period.

"Pure pretentiousness! With his esoteric ways, he would make AA a society of ascetics if you gave him the chance."

He knew she resented Chris because the younger man, a mere alcoholic, presumed to have discovered some vital truth about religion of which she, life-long practicing Christian that she was, had been ignorant, and she would not accept that.

He himself had experienced something of the same discord during the post-Towns era when her joy at his sobriety contended with her discovery that a so-called mystical experience had been the alleged source of it.

His own Lois, he brooded—so conventional, so unadventurous in her thinking: *our* way, *my* way—the true way, the only way.

It was the same even in AA. There, as everywhere, the tyranny of the majority prevailed. One must not be too different. Fortunately AAs soft-pedalled their judgment lest the individual in question, resentful and isolated, drink as a result.

But Chris had gone beyond AA and in that sense Lois' comment about his not being a "real member" was right. Swept into the movement in the great outpouring after the 1941 Alexander article, he had absorbed what the program could offer him for a year or two, going almost every night to meetings for the first six months; then, with the help of spiritual experiences unknown to most AAs, including himself, had moved with inevitable steps into the world of yoga and mysticism, where for at least six years now he had found a comfortable place.

Because their friendship had been well established when he left AA—though in the deepest sense he could not be said to have "left" at all—they had maintained their periodic contact ever since, and Chris' desire to complete his biography, which he was threatening to call *Reluctant Prophet,* was still ongoing. Bill was happy about their association, Chris filling a special role in his life, like a personification of conscience ... even though he irritated him at times, made him impatient, forgetting—or seeming to—his unique position, his responsibility to the whole fellowship, his utter inability to act for himself alone but always to measure everything he did—certainly the consequences of such a step as Chris urged upon him—by its likely effect on the morale of thousands of members.

Once-born like Dr. Bob though they were, despite their years of sobriety.

But what about himself?

Was he, too, despite Towns, once-born, even after fifteen years of sobriety ... or was he still, at the age of fifty-three, capable of the authentic new birth that Chris Eastman had known?

He felt his spiritual state was half-way between the possibilities represented, on the one hand, by Chris and the Princess and, on the other, by Dr. Bob and Lois and most of his AA acquaintance.

From the beginning that had been his role, as mediator between disparate temperaments and viewpoints and for the most part, even during the trauma that had seized him for these five years, it had been maintained successfully.

But now?

Had a new era really dawned, for him and for the fellowship—or was he being carried away by unacknowledged *hubris*, by the secret gratifications implicit in Chris' call to the mystical path?

At times he thought one thing, at other times another.

What troubled him throughout his ruminations was the persistent consciousness of the state he was in, and *had* been in so long: the depression that hamstrung all his efforts—sporadic and tentative as they were—to rouse his dormant energies.

His condition was like—it *was*—a tangible face of that ego, that power of darkness, the foe of regenerate life which indiscriminately had hounded him through fifteen years of drinking and then with equal menace through the same length of time sober, *merely manifesting* in different ways—the depression being (as he was now sure) the reflection of that demonic element made visible.

The depression did indeed seem to be *the ego itself,* blocking his means of escape, preventing Chris' ideas—or any other that might point him in a new direction—from bearing fruit.

He felt haunted by this conception of ego—implacable enemy, unique benefactor. His exercise of memory had led to *it* as the reality! Perhaps *that* was the discovery to be made: that his unshakable depression was truly the ego, the demonic, the mystery incarnate!

Excited, he arrested his thought, reached gropingly for his journal, again declined to make use of it, content to let the ideas possess him, rising to his feet as he did so, moving—somber, tense, yet elated—towards the door, which he opened, like opening his mind to the idea, then stepped outside into the cool bath of the midsummer evening enveloping everything in its spell. He breathed deeply, feeling his aloneness match the solitary nature of his thought. He stretched as though expanding his mind to a new conception.

He still felt the weight of his depressed condition—it would not be so easily dislodged. But it cohabited now—for how long he could not guess—with a flowing vitality of knowledge: the insight that had come to him.

Why search the past if it was—as he had concluded—so unreliable? Why?—For discoveries like *this*!

Then a counter-movement in his thought assailed him, affecting him like a dash of cold water in his face.

It was a great discovery, yes. But it was still the ego dominating him, *straddling* him, suffocating him with the atmosphere of the depression—*its* creation.

His new knowledge had not—would likely not—lift the incubus. Some other means, or power, would have to accomplish that.

Even after he knew more about its nature than his psychiatrist, it was still there! Under different forms it had been with him, perhaps, all the time since that day on County Street. Even during the triumphant AA years it had obviously been his constant witness.

That he had discovered what it was, and what his depression really was—though a victory in its own right—only made more frightening than ever the power and cunning of his adversary. (In the Big Book he had attributed this baffling power to alcohol, but now he knew better. It was the *mind*—the *ego's* mind—that had the cunning and the mystery.)

So much so that even his fresh awareness, the fruit of this day's contemplation, might only be feeding the ego all over again!

He would not give up, but in a final analysis it would probably take a saint to work successfully through this labyrinth of cause and effect—of knowledge, knower, and the thing known.

He breathed deeply again of the grass and flowering life secret in the gathering dusk. The early evening settled gratefully around him, the summer silences blended in a quiet bucolic symphony that soothed the note of confusion that had shaken the current of his thought.

Seated again in his chair in the studio hideaway, he felt his mind taking hold, in weighing once more, as he had so often, Chris Eastman's argument that spiritual life alone was the answer.

Again the question kept revolving: To do or not to do. To be or not to be. For in such new doing there would no doubt emerge new being.

The New Man. Becoming *in fact* what he had drunk to attain.

There was the record in his favor. Towns chiefly. But also those intermittent *aperçus* in Vermont in the early years. And the moments in Winchester Cathedral and at Newport during the war. For certain, he had the *potential* for the mystic path.

Again: was he denying himself the realization of his whole life's longings by temporizing ... by, in fact, *allowing the depression to continue* ... for there was little doubt by now that *he* was fully responsible for its onset, its continuance, its depth.

Could he not, then, unseat it, banish it?

After what he knew about its true nature and origin, *what it really was in disguised form*—could he not?

Anxiously he realized that that very knowledge of what it was— its hidden birth in the dark womb of egoism—had set up a new and subtle barrier to its dissolution, made its weight suddenly more oppressive, bringing to the fore once again the mood of hopelessness to lift the burden—which seemed a life-sentence passed against him, compelling him to bear it.

Drinking ... Ego ... Depression....

It was an equation that could be applied to many things, throwing light into obscure corners.

For example, it was often thought that alcoholism led to brain damage. But with his recent awareness he guessed it was the *ego,* the dark presence, that caused it.

Drinking was merely the way the ego chose to bring about the disintegration of the personality and defeat its search for self-identity.

As, in a different season, the depression was another such, geared to the same objective.

This insight, unknown to him before today, and still strange, electric, he handled with instinctive care, retracing it carefully through the circuits of his brain in a quiet effort to make it part of his knowledge, without fear of losing it.

In attempting to "banish" the depression, consequently, he would be attempting to unseat the presence of death from his life, the power of pure evil.

Again his thinking came to a sudden halt as, shuddering, he felt the force of this drastic conclusion.

No wonder he had had such difficulty with it. No wonder it had clung to him for so long!

How, he asked himself with sudden urgency, *could* he unseat this spiritual beast that had taken possession of his life to a degree surpassing the influence of alcohol even in the worst of the old days?

If he had the will to do so, if he wanted to, and if it was possible … *how?*

By knowledge?

Knowledge, he had found, was by no means enough. Knowledge was powerful when desire for freedom had *first* liberated you. Otherwise it only made more miserable your bondage: his own condition. Even the knowledge that had come to him this day, transcending the psychological categories with which he had become so familiar from Dr. Tiebout, would not be enough. For one good reason: the *will* had to be engaged, which knowledge—at least as he had experienced it— failed to accomplish.

Knowledge was humanist, intellectual, but the problem with which he had to cope was mysterious, oddly *spiritual* in its nature. Therefore, some approach either directly spiritual or *involving* the spiritual element had to be employed.

What had worked so wondrously for him in the thirties. But now?

Now he doubted that it would work for one very good reason.

He had not prayed in over a year, perhaps two years.

It was a secret no one knew. Not Lois, not Chris, not Dr. Bob of course. Bob least of all. As he reflected now, the thought of the absence of prayer from his life for so long all at once terrified him. But, equally, *the thought of prayer itself did.*

The feeling he had was similar to his resistance to the whole notion of prayer during the early thirties.

For the act of prayer brought his mind unavoidably into the ego's realm, into the very regions of his psyche whence had come, with such all-blanketing force, the deadening pall of his depression; compelled him to cope with inner realities that were simply too much for him—or that he was convinced were.

There were the mechanical prayers, rote exercises with Lois at stated times continuing a marital practice of years (mostly simple audible invocations), and of course the Paternoster at the end of those meetings in the last year or two he was able to attend.

There were these kinds of "prayers," but nothing *serious,* nothing suggesting *belief* in what he was doing. Nothing like those prayers he made, with such liberating success, during his first year of sobriety, prayers made as if his life depended on them: as indeed it had.

He could not remember the last time he made such a prayer.

Five years, at least. Perhaps much longer!

Just as alcoholism precluded spiritual life, *presumed* essential atheism, so depression did the same. The person depressed at *his* level, and for so long a period, was *ipso facto* an unbeliever. For the mindset of depression *was* that of doubt, faithlessness, godlessness.

How foolish to think he could cope with the presence of a form of death on his spirit—on every part of him: body, mind, nerves—when he could not even pray, lacked the will to energize his powers even to the extent of a simple, heartfelt prayer whose efficacy, he well knew, was not to be doubted.

How unrealistic to forget the actual depths of his apathy, his malaise, his lack of *force* ... lacking the necessary resources, at any rate their *availability,* for confronting whatever it was that had seized his life for so long and what, if anything, he was going to do about it.

Knowledge of his condition would not suffice for what was needed: will.

But the will to do anything about it was missing. Even the will to pray.

There it was in all its starkness.

He craved to feel a sudden surge of death-daring energy, a ruthless inward drive of *will*power, a violent rush of resolution to sweep away his lassitude—a force generated, paradoxically, by knowledge: knowledge of his incapability to free himself by knowledge alone, *this* knowledge illuminating his need, the facts of his impotence, the self-stultification in which he labored.

An all-conquering will to overcome himself at whatever cost!

12   Lois and The Phantom years

He felt stirred at depth, wishing Lois were here so he might share this moment of hope. So often she saw him in an opposite state and sometimes seemed to contract a kind of passing depression herself.

He got up and looked toward the house. Because of the problems of organizing the first few alcoholic families, paralleling AA itself, she could be very late. He admired her initiative in tackling this much-needed work, bringing the insights of AA, as well as her own experience in coping with an addict, to spouses of alcoholics, battered by the disease often as much as the addicts themselves.[*]

In addition, it took her out of the house more often and gave her something else to occupy her mind besides worrying about his condition.

He was glad he had left the lights on. Everything about the house to a potential intruder looked normal, and to Lois' eyes upon returning there would be the welcome sight of a familiar scene.

To his eyes, as well, the house assumed the aspect of something intimately known, the quiet semi-secluded fortress that meant security

---

[*] The family groups of alcoholics that Lois helped to establish would soon be known as Al-Anon.

and peace after the instability of the two years preceding their move there in 1941, the period after they had been evicted from Clinton Street for insolvency.

A widowed older woman, as a token of her gratitude for what AA had done for a close friend of hers, had offered them the house for a minimum monthly payment, with nothing down. They had seen in the gesture the working of providence compensating them for the life they had lived in AA.

Now it stood there, brown-shingled, nestled in a slight hollow amid its bower of tree and shrubbery against a sloping wooded background, silent, warm and inviting in the summer dark.

Lois Burnham Wilson...

She was closest to him of anyone, and it had been so ever since their days at Emerald Lake. But how little she really knew of him. His drinking had been a mystery to her ("If you could see the way you look when you drink you would never touch alcohol again!"). The discovery of AA had been another mystery, bringing him to sobriety when her prayers and sacrifices and her love had failed to do so. And now this depression the deepest mystery of all, the one that seemed to humiliate her in a peculiar way: Bill Wilson living with a devoted wife and depressed for nearly six years—how could that be?

Vanity notwithstanding, she had always been his mainstay, the silver lining in the persistent black cloud that was most of his life through the late twenties and early thirties, his stalwart helpmate through every crisis, the one bright spot in his memory of those tunnel-driven days....

Lois, his fate: the embodiment of the design that was his life. Which he could still affirm even in the midst of the apathetic gloom that had become his staple. The design whose awareness had taught him that everything that had happened to him was in the final analysis good, including the worst of times—for everything had led to AA.

Though Lois' contribution to his life was still strong, her greatest help had been felt in the years leading up to Towns: that island of chimerical, fantastic time recalled now as having almost happened to someone else. It was as though those fifteen years prior to 1934 had been lived all at once, the way things happen in dreams, everything merging in a shadowland of unreality.

Through it all the unforgettable figure of Lois at his side. Standing out in bold relief because of the truth she represented—everything else by comparison shadow, untruth.

Lois central to the design. There was the matter of her pregnancies, for example.

One of her heartbreaks had been the realization, following three ectopic pregnancies, that she could not have children. After her last confinement she had learned that her Fallopian tubes had been blocked since birth ... which meant she had been marked out, intended to live for him and with him *alone,* that the design for their two lives had been completed even then, just as Mark Whalon had guessed something of the same while standing outside the Wilson House on that howling night long ago. Due to Bill's drinking problem adoption was not feasible either.

No children were allowed. He recalled Francis Bacon's aphorism, that a man with children gives hostages to fortune. When he and Lois met she entered a domain of fate. A mighty enterprise lay ahead of her: to be his support through the long storm of his alcoholism.

All her energies were needed for *that* challenge.

Her chief task: making sure he stayed alive long enough to receive the revelation and the mission.

Without her he would have succumbed to alcohol with no supporting help to look for outside the drinking experience. *With* her he would have succumbed, as he did, but have *her* to turn to when he recovered.

As he had always known, a more sensitive woman, like Bertha, would have recoiled in horror at his alcoholism and fled. It was because Lois—again, as part of the design—lacked that extra degree of sensitivity that she was able to keep herself in the place assigned her, with all its trials.

In short, her force of character—strong and balanced, resourceful enough even without inspiration from beyond to prevail for a whole lifetime—counterbalanced his own volatility, was a match for his downward-driving obsession ... a power for stability at war with a power for instability. A clash of wills. The question for a long time was: which would outlast the other? And the answer came, eventually, loud and clear: his will to fail was outlasted by hers to endure.

The design was also evident even in the work she pursued in the early twenties—in occupational therapy, first with the Red Cross at a veteran's hospital, later in the women's psychiatric ward at Bellevue (where she encountered many alcoholics)—service well suited to her maternal and practical nature. It was work which, as he saw so clearly now, but not then, prepared her for the day of finding an unending succession of strangers, some sober, some not, in her own house ... prepared her for *him* as well, the stranger-spouse she found herself married to.

Prepared her for the horrors of the phantom years, for the bearing up under so many blows to her faith.

His broken vows, his failures, his endless derelictions.

There was much to bear as he seemed determined to defeat that faith in their battle of wills, and she determined to withstand him.

There had been a time when he wondered how his years in an environment so hectic and ego-feeding as Wall Street could have served any purpose in a higher design, but he had come to see that its very unreality, its power to fill him with flamboyant, narcissistic dreams of secret influence, accelerated the decline into his own unreality, gave him little or nothing substantial to cling to that might have slowed his drift to disintegration.

Even the preliminary job he found by 1921 that led him directly to his career as self-anointed guru of the stock market was tailored to bring him to his point of no return in as brief a time as possible, and by the shortest route: with a company that investigated default of firms on the stock exchange for fraud and embezzlement. The prospects this job held out were exciting, it offered him undercover entrée into the financial world, where, he had intuited at once, lay his real destiny.

As he saw it, the work would make him in time a familiar face in the dense web of Wall Street where gradually he would develop contacts which later would prove valuable when he set himself up as an independent operator—the brilliant Lone Wolf of the Street. He would learn how deals were made, how fortunes were won, and lost, why some succeeded, and others failed. Without anyone realizing it, he would make himself an insider in the most challenging of all arenas.

By the mid-twenties he had emerged as a securities analyst and was soon enjoying an enviable reputation for a solid and original grasp of the mysteries of the stock market. Around that time he took an exploratory trip to various parts of the country to investigate at first hand the stability and economic prospects of firms he would advise his clients for or against. It was a shrewd plan, which appealed to Lois as well because of their mutual love of travel and unfamiliar scenes, refreshing their spirits, after their long immersion in urban atmospheres, at the fountain of Nature's bounty. In addition he did not seem to need alcohol during these rural excursions.

In the excitement of his new ambition his drinking had advanced by precipitous stages. Sensing the insidious progression of his problem, he still refused to recognize it as such. Meanwhile Lois no longer thought that living with her would be such an inspiration he would never even think of alcohol. One Christmas, he remembered, they had a heart-to-heart discussion about the matter (one of innumerable talks to follow), as a result of which he made a vow, solemnly recording the moment in her family Bible, never to drink again ... remaining sober that time for two full months.

Beginning to panic secretly but still convinced that reason, experiment, and willpower in combination would prevail and he would drink normally ... an egomaniac confidence fueled by the grandiosity of his dreams of triumph among the canyons of greed.

Intrigued by his own cultivated image: a hooded, impulse-driven Wall Street operator shrouded in an aura of mysterious sources of information, like a bird of passage flitting among the brokerages and investment firms, analyst *extraordinary,* taking no root, dropping in here, inquiring there, availing himself of ticker tapes wherever he went, a ghost among the predators, polishing, *romanticizing* his image ... peculiarly wearing his hat indoors at all times—a badge of his vagrant life, disdaining an office as befitted a man of mystery, a mercurial loner, his office the nearest phone booth, preferably in the nearest speakeasy ... steadily rising to notice, then to notoriety, because of his forecasts, but never able to exploit his success or persevere in one direction, oscillating in his plans, moods, expectations constantly, and little by little coming to be known for such among his peers ... all the while, in season and out, daily drinking, except when periodic excesses led to forced interludes of dryness, building up his momentum for the next and inevitable breakout, one of those times being Lois' third ectopic pregnancy, when he neglected her during her days in the hospital; another the death of her mother in 1930, when he failed to put in an appearance at the funeral ... but Lois still hoping, still trusting in him after all the vows made, then broken, all the times she found him in the small hours of the morning in the front hall of the Clinton Street house asleep on the stone floor.

When his income became insufficient to support them—due to waning influence in the Street as news of his drinking pattern spread—Lois began her long career working in department stores ... always, he knew, the desperate fear clutching at her heart, a feeling of disaster impending all the time, even during relatively quiet and dry periods.

He too visited by the same fears—what if they lost it all, their hopes and dreams, their reason for being together? *It could happen.*

But he could not retain the awareness.

In the end only one thing mattered, one thing alone was significant: the drug of his addiction.

They tried everything. With the naiveté of the nonalcoholic, Lois made suggestions he enthusiastically adopted, their experiments based on the hope that the problem stemmed from certain suspect conditions and consequently its solution lay in manipulating these externals into a more rational pattern. He would drink only beer or wine, would take a vow not to drink for a month, would drink only after twelve noon, would never drink on an empty stomach, would swallow a few drops of apple cider vinegar before he began to drink.

Nothing worked.

With time, it had become clear why the effect of alcohol upon his system was so crucial: it bridged the two worlds of fantasy and reality— rather, brought the outer into the inner, making it conform to the parameters of his dream life.

Even the *thought* of alcohol could almost produce the same effect, he reflected now, fixing his mind again on the profound psychic change drinking and its prospect had had upon him, and dwelling not so much on the promiscuous succession of drinking bouts—all testifying to the steady and fatal advance year by year—as upon the *character change* that alcohol had wrought in him from the first time at the Grinnells'.

The infallible sign of the alcoholic. Some drank different forms of alcohol, some drank daily while others did not, some were disgraced by their drinking while others were not, some drank alone, some always with others, but all alike suffered a *sea change* in their personality the moment they took the first drink.

That was the essential knowledge he and Lois lacked.

One particular discovery puzzled and alarmed him: when, after a period of abstinence, he returned to the habit, it had become, each time, *progressively worse,* as though he had been drinking every day of the dry spell.

He recalled Fulton Sheen's dictum, resented at the time, that alcoholism was a *moral disease.* Unhappily, the cleric had been right— it was. Like a secret vice to a mystic enlightened about his problem, so that with time the slightest return to *his* addiction would have increasingly painful and enervating consequences. It was a moral prerequisite that he stop drinking for the same reason. The *progressive* character of the compulsion was to alert him to the fact that what he was doing had grave spiritual dangers.

Dangers not only to his physical existence....

The only true respite, at least during the twenties, came during their periodic excursions to the country, often far from the New York area, sometimes combining the pleasure of the experience with his intermittent investigations at the actual site of companies listed on the stock exchange. Occasionally during these camping trips he seemed to banish the thought of alcohol from his mind when they occupied themselves as a team with ideas, moods, and adventures utterly at variance from their urban life. They rode his motorcycle, with Lois in the sidecar; or they hitchhiked, or took buses; now and then drove a car of their own. Whatever their means of transportation, they traveled far and wide, equal in their love of the country, so rejuvenating themselves that both came to believe during these times that the fears that had hounded them in New York were once and for all overcome.

They would lie on the ground and sing songs together, cultivating their mutual love of music, both popular and classical, that had become one of their chief bonds. She was adept at the piano and he still played the violin whenever possible. Several times they went to East Dorset, where they visited his grandparents, After the death of both old people early in the twenties they sojourned once more at Emerald Lake and renewed private memories of their premarital vows.

Each time they made contact with Mark Whalon, happy as always to see them, now contentedly taken up with the life of a rural letter-carrier. He had no desire, he said, to visit New York for any reason. "Been reading lately a certain Oswald Spengler, a German writer, who says that in the final stages in the decline of a culture everybody flees like lemmings to the cities, especially the 'world city', as he calls it, of each country. I want no part of that kind of migration...."

Mark was right. Why couldn't he have been satisfied with a more modest arena in which to live out his life? Why was the largest stage so necessary? And then, his drinking always ebbed, almost disappeared, whenever they visited the country. He knew that all too well. It was as if he *had* to continue with what he was doing, playing a role in a script already written. East Dorset was not possible for him any more.

As though reading his mind, Mark went on: "But that's *my* lookout, Will! *You* need New York, I believe, for what you must do— need the biggest sounding-board. Be patient with him, Lois, because the great world is going to hear of him one of these days!"

Calmed and reassured by the therapy of the trip, she found it natural to smile in agreement. "There's no doubt in my mind either!"

But there was in his own, much doubt. Much anxiety, confusion, and fear.

They went back to their routine. The very hour of their return, while she was shopping, he was in a speakeasy, inviting the enemy.

It seemed that on the subconscious level his sobriety was *planned* ... so that, once back in the city, he could resume what he was living for and, after the rural respite, be able to do so with a good conscience and the self-assurance that, though he might be drinking again, and getting drunk again too, he had established an undeniable record of sobriety to which, when he *really* needed to, he could confidently return at *any* time.

The net result, however, was that the Jekyll-and-Hyde syndrome advanced week by week. Lois could, to a degree, protect him from many things but not from himself, not from the demons of his own making.

Especially the demon of rationalization.

By the early thirties his reputation had been ruined on the Street. Over and over he repudiated solemn promises for the sake of one last drink. Because his financial associates did not see in him anything beyond what met the eye, they had no incentive to remain faithful to him. He became unemployable. Debts confronted him at every turn.

Blackouts were a recurrent feature of his drinking now, the most alarming part of it all. He felt as though he was losing his grip on his mind.

Both to save money, and by choice, he had become a lone drinker.

In the spring of 1933 Lois' widowed father remarried and left them the Clinton Street property. It was like a godsend, the answer to whatever prayer he was able to make. Now they had not only the second floor but the whole house to themselves. He was able to spend all his time drinking, hiding bottles everywhere, living in pajamas and bathrobe. As a result his drinking, far advanced as it had been, rapidly deteriorated. Fortunately Lois' job in the department store remained intact. Without her income they would have been penniless.

The suicidal mood was frequent with him now, drinking or dry. Lois grew as desperate as he. The time for camping trips was long past—something more drastic was called for. In the fall of 1933 she contacted Bill's sister and her husband, Leonard Strong, an osteopath, and related the horror story. The Strongs, New York residents, promptly recommended a stay in Towns Hospital on Central Park West. They would pay the expenses. It was a drying-out hospital.

There would be subsequent visits and the treatment was expensive. The Strongs could not absorb all the costs. Dorothy had to notify her mother for help.

Dr. William Silkworth was the chief physician in attendance, a small, white-haired man with a deep personal interest in alcoholism and sympathy for its victims. He had concluded that it was a disease whose only cure was for the afflicted individual to abstain totally from alcohol in any form at all times. It was a physical allergy linked with an obsession to drink which doomed the victim ultimately to the direst kind of fate.

There was a vast feeling of relief upon hearing this interpretation of the scourge that was killing him. Alcoholism was a disease like any other—there was nothing moral about it, nothing connected with a lack of willpower. It was another kind of cancer!

There was no stigma attached to it, nothing to do with weakness of character or of will.

He felt like a new man, with a great burden lifted from his life. The problem of his drinking seemed solved in one stroke. Now that he knew what the facts were, including the all-important need of abstaining from alcohol at all times, he could live like others, liberated from fear, from shame, from terror, from thoughts of suicide.

In retrospect, however, Silkworth's theory had been too good to be true. There *was,* he knew (now at least), an irreducible moral factor. Both approaches contributed to an understanding of the problem, both—medical and moral—were necessary. But now he believed that the medical was merely the *way,* the *medium,* by which the moral principle manifested.

Moreover, if the medical or scientific interpretation alone was the correct one, why was a regenerative way of life necessary if the recovering alcoholic was to stay not only sober but serene, stable, and happy in his new state—as was indubitably the experience of AA everywhere? The backbone of the AA way of life, the Twelve Steps, made practically no mention of alcohol but was confined instead to a progressively more moral and conscientious, ethical lifestyle, and assumed as a working premise that the nature of the alcoholic was fundamentally a moral and spiritual one.

Relieved nevertheless by the Silkworth analysis, he seemed to find a more solid kind of sobriety after leaving Towns.

It lasted two months.

How to live happily apart from alcohol, how to stay away from that first drink... were questions the Silkworth theory had *not* covered.

The last year of his drinking and the tense, dry intervals between, from the end of 1933 to the end of 1934, was the most confused and dislocated in his memory. The obsession accelerated by leaps and bounds—the two months' sobriety only seeming to have maddened the frustrated addict that slept within. In desperation Lois quit her job to accompany him on another camping trip in the hope of giving him a chance to re-experience his better self, but on this occasion her hopes were dashed. Whenever the opportunity arose, he drank and got drunk.

And when in the spring they returned to the city, once again—only more compulsively than ever—he resumed his alcoholic ways, while Lois, to support them, found another job in a Brooklyn department store close to home.

How many more times was he hospitalized at Towns that year? Two at least, perhaps three. Terrified, drawing no comfort now from the Silkworth thesis, and not surprised when he heard from Lois what the little doctor, when she had pressed him for some answers, or at least some guidance, had been forced to tell her: that alcoholism had thoroughly mastered her husband, that unless he was permanently incarcerated—*put away*—his drinking would very soon lead only to insanity or death. There was nothing else she could look forward to.

Silkworth no alarmist, a man of sober, measured phrases. She never thought of challenging him. Nor did her husband.

So it was ending, what had begun at Emerald Lake with such faith and idealism. The dream turned to nightmare.

The knowledge that his mother had had to pay for his hospitalization did not shame or humiliate him. He did not react to the news, though once he would have found it insupportable: his condition triumphant proof that he would never after all amount to anything, that he was just as weak and inadequate as she had always believed he was. Her involvement did not faze him, could not penetrate the ring of fear within which he lay trapped, beaten, dehumanized.

13 The Moment at Towns

What occurred at Towns that night in December—the moment of his life—did not happen spontaneously. A process was at work, initiated long before. Both spiritual and mundane factors were linked as a prelude. Prior to the otherworldly moment there were this-worldly elements involved—naturalistic, relevant, and logical. There was a sequence of forces at play.

His reading, for one thing. For at least two years preceding he had been attracted to self-help books of all kinds, from works that promoted regimens of self-worth by autosuggestion ("Everyday in every way I am getting better and better") to the Christian Science textbook, *Science and Health,* which he read from cover to cover at least twice, typically while unshaven, dressed in pajamas, seated at the kitchen table in the Clinton Street house, nursing drink after drink of gin through the long, lurid hours.

Works on alcoholism intrigued him as well, drawing him in the vain hope of finding through rational inquiry an answer to his problem. Only another alcoholic, he brooded, could come close to providing such an answer but none of *them* were writing books.

Then there was the Silkworth warning to Lois about the inevitability of being locked up, the looming *necessity* of it. His brain, he told her, was damaged, his life hanging by a thread. There was nothing further he, Silkworth, could do for him. Nothing anyone could do.

So, while the terror invaded him, and while there was still *some* time, or seemed to be, he read and reread his self-help books, or the alcoholic studies, like a man searching a map for an escape from some impregnable prison; and finding no way out, with a sense of greater bondage than ever.

Integral to the sequence was the November 1934 visit, after the unexpected phone call of an old drinking companion, a deep-dyed alcoholic, Ebby Thatcher, whom he had not seen in five years. Thatcher had heard about his problems on Wall Street and resolved to bring to his door the good news of his own recovery from their common enemy. He brushed off the suggestion of a drink to celebrate their reunion in the Clinton Street kitchen.

"I don't need to drink any more," he said. And when pressed for an explanation, answered simply that he "had got religion" through the medium of the Oxford Group.

This was a well-known, evangelical, and proselytizing movement marked by crusading zeal and high, ethical principles. It did not concentrate its efforts on alcoholics but at the same time did not exclude them from their organizational embrace. Ebby Thatcher had found that embrace warm, nourishing, transforming. They had taught him the necessity of being honest with himself and of the vital role of prayer as the chief means to liberation from sin and vice.

Prayer would be answered, they had told him. Ebby the drinking skeptic had doubted them, but had tried, and it had succeeded. In a short time he looked and felt like a new man and was, above all, happy in his sobriety.

And convincing, with none of the convert's passion diluting the impression of truth and sincerity.

In the light of remembrance he recalled Ebby's later reversion to drinking, getting sober over and over—never quite winning, never quite losing. But during the encounter at Clinton Street all he knew was that Ebby Thatcher, once a sodden addict as hopeless as anyone he had ever drunk with—more afflicted even than himself—was a changed and happy man, and in a final analysis prayer was the power that had salvaged him.

He might regret that, but he could not deny the evidence of his senses.

All the more persuasive because of the vise of fear and terror that held him.

The Towns experience at the end of the year seemed to signify that the life he was living was an outer manifestation of some mysterious drama of the Secret Self where everything was first perfected in a hidden realm of transcendental Intelligence before appearing in the deceptive garments of a "Life."

The experience was indescribably single and solitary, giving him a sudden glimpse of that secret world in action, revealing itself to his mind never before so unmistakably.

There was the self and its consciousness ... then there was everything else.

Life as a Dream.

He searched back, his thoughts paused, the room grew still.

It had lasted no more than a minute, perhaps as little as ten or fifteen seconds, but had endured because of its truth-content, its grounding in the authentically real, as opposed to all the moments of his life lived in dream-like reality.

After the cry into the dark, the thrust of his will into the center of his unknown mind, there was the sudden peace, the light, the assurance. The strangeness and at the same time the familiarity—coming into his own home, his true realm. Once there, it was as though he had never left.

But difficult to recover. The memory lay beneath increasingly heavy layers of myriads of impressions—to be recaptured with greater difficulty all the time. Never lost altogether but more and more elusive ... like something he had betrayed and would not easily be won again.

Those earlier moments in Winchester Cathedral, and at Newport and Emerald Lake, had qualified him for the lightning-strike at Towns, but he had gravely mishandled it—to such a degree that it was remarkable that nothing worse than this depression—horrendous as it was—had befallen him.

His maladroit management of the experience of his life was sufficient proof of his unfitness for any new path which Chris held out to him.

His biggest mistake was that he had blunted the uniqueness of the experience by his compulsion to talk about it, year after year. No one, it is true, was there to give him guidance. Pressed for a candid response, Chris had admitted it was "inappropriate" for anyone to talk freely about a mystical encounter intended to be shared exclusively with the divine.

Why had he done so? In the early period with Silkworth, with Lois, with members of the Oxford Group, with Ebby of course, later with innumerable AA members at scores of meetings, and in written form over and over, commencing with the Big Book, and in other places. Why? Down deep, he was certain, he had really *known* how to handle it, for would not someone to whom the experience was given also inevitably receive the grace to know how to manage it in relation to others?

Now, he believed, the ego had turned even that moment, perhaps especially that, to its own advantage. In sum, he had talked about the experience ... *deliberately*.

Talked about it in order to lose it—and all but succeeded.

Inappropriate? Chris, out of deference, had been too gentle with him.

He had told the story so often it had become trivialized. He had become like an actor mouthing merely words, of no significance, indulging the less spiritual of the AA membership by the "hot flash" pacifier!

He had emptied himself, ignorantly demeaning the high point of his life.

He had *exploited* the experience, had not nursed and protected it, nor attempted to understand it.

He had not served it, but had made it serve *him*.

Unlike St. Paul, he suddenly remembered, rising slowly to his feet and picking out his Bible from the small shelf of choice volumes he had brought with him to the studio. He found the passage he had in mind. *Galatians* 1: 16–18. St. Paul, after *his* experience: "—immediately I conferred not with flesh and blood.... but I went into Arabia ... then after three years I went up to Jerusalem to see Peter..."

Chris had explained the passage to him once. It meant that after the light broke upon him along the Damascus Road, Paul fled from the society of men for three years in the desert of Arabia in order to understand what had happened to him, to make that new reality not only part of his total consciousness but the very ground of it, to bring the creaturely part of his character—which prior to Damascus had been so strong and self-serving—into concordance with, and submission to, the birth of the New Man which had begun, but no more than begun, during those moments of the revelation.

Unlike the Apostle, he had merely followed his instincts, dominated even then by his own powerful self-loving creatureliness, now enthroned on the heights of the moment of truth given him, and utilizing that moment for its own headstrong purposes. In short, he had not remained *alone* with the experience and with the power behind it.

True, he had spent some days intensely reading the seminal work Ebby had given him at Towns, William James' *Varieties,* and while the aura of the moment was still fresh—unassisted by anything *he* had done to deepen and internalize it—he had rationally tried to comprehend the whole meaning of James' "psychology of conversion."

But that had faded. Soon he was back within the confines of his old self—with a difference, naturally, but still without any kind of disciplined or enlightened effort to unite his full mind with what had happened. His ambition to be Number One had quickly reasserted itself and he was sure he could be first among all hopeless drunks in the country—all *former* victims, at any rate—and on the strength of what had been given to him he would rush forth to create an endless train of recovering alcoholics, with himself in the lead!

In a word, he had *used* the experience to serve his self-interest, his creature desires ... though no doubt those were worthy desires.

He had in effect *ruled* it, had not allowed it to rule *him.*

But if he had done what Chris would have advised, there very likely would have been no AA. He would have advanced himself spiritually, but at what a cost!

So what was the answer?

He had done what he had to do, and the result had been the birth of Alcoholics Anonymous.

He was, he knew all over again, nothing special as a man, as a soul. He was Everyman ... a common everyday man, easily matched, singled out for the momentous gift that had been showered on him ... but singled out, perhaps, for his very ordinariness, so that others—few of them distinguished or illustrious minds (allowing for exceptions like Chris Eastman)—would see themselves in him, as indeed they had.

In a final analysis he had done the right thing. Even the constant speech-making and his uncounted references to the "hot flash," he was sure now, had been right, had done much good, had made it possible, for one thing, to lay stress on the spiritual nature of the AA program: there he stood before them, living proof of its validity.

He had not gone the way Chris and the Princess and a few others, like the California mystics Gerald Heard, Isherwood and Huxley, would have wanted him to go, had failed to develop himself as a spiritual personality to the degree they were certain he could have done, but even now, still feeling something of the undoubted attraction in their appeal, he did not regret anything. He had been forced to sacrifice his own spiritual development for the sake of others' sobriety—untold numbers of them, who unmistakably would turn away from AA as it would have become—a fellowship for the saintly and the mystical—if he had not chosen the course he had, and hewed to it.

These ruminations had taken their toll, working on his energy levels like a succession of physical blows, leaving him weary, drained. After putting the Bible back on the shelf he stood abstracted with thought in the middle of the darkening studio room, staring, half-seeing, toward the house across the way; then gravitated, suddenly depleted, and worn-out, back to the swivel chair, his movements slow, awkward, like an invalid's.

Which is what I am. He had to face it. Fifty-three years old. An *old* fifty-three. Not a man young for those years, as he would have had to be to truly qualify for Chris' spiritual ideal. A man old for his years. An old man masquerading as a forceful leader of a world movement, with so many depending on his guidance, so many being deceived.

Himself, first of all.

Whatever it *really* was that had him in its grip had affected more than his state of *mind*. It had ruled his bodily life as well, manifesting as inertia, often a strange, threatening immobility, a kind of semi-paralysis of will to galvanize his body into making more than the most rudimentary actions.

He looked outside again, through the window directly in front of him as he sat at the desk. Soon he would *try* to take that walk, *try* once again to assert mastery where so often another master—whose name he did not know—had established itself.

St. Paul.... His thoughts revolved again about the figure of the Apostle. Instinctively he had compared himself to him, while six years ago, at the height of his AA activity and before the miasma of inertia had besieged him, it would never have occurred to him to do so. *Now* it had, in the midst of his retreat from life. As though to compensate? A secret device of the ego to gain the most out of the very condition it had pressed down upon him?

Whatever the truth was, there were points of resemblance ... as well, of course, as major differences. Both had received sudden illuminations, making believers and tireless workers and visionaries out of them. Each then became the founder of a worldwide movement, preacher in each instance to a vast multitude.

He did not think comparing AA—as it had become in the last eight years and gave promise soon of far surpassing itself—to the beginnings of Christianity was far-fetched. Indeed AA, a fraternity of addicts, was a perfect equivalent to Paul's communion of sinners standing every moment, as did the recovering alcoholic more than most, in need of grace, who, like Paul's new-born Christian, had to reinvent himself day by day, had to continue to *earn* his salvation—or his sobriety—on a daily basis. Paul had described the New Man—or, nearer home, the recovering addict—as one "who was sometime *darkness*," lacking light, power, or means to save himself from the condition he was in, the man he *was*—an accurate reading of the alcoholic in his active mode. And there was the passage from Romans, which spoke so well to his own condition: "For the good I would do, I do not; but the evil I would not do, that I do."

No group of converts Paul ever taught came as close to the reality of his description of man-the-lost-soul in his natural state as the members of an AA group anywhere in the country. Lost ... but found. Wicked ... but reborn. Damned ... but saved. Sinners but *admitted* sinners, struggling with their new consciousness, their emerging souls.

How many "Christians" thought of themselves as AAs did—their lives constantly in jeopardy, subject to innumerable chances of ruin and disaster at every hour of the day or night ... a condition caused not by outer forces but by their own unregeneracy? How many knew themselves as they truly were? How many—as every AA did sooner or later—saw the ego at work in all its multiple destructive guises?

He and the Apostle had some things in common and, in truth, the role he had played with AA could best be described as that of an apostle himself. But some things they did *not* have in common.

The key difference between them was that Paul, after *his* enlighten-ment, had *persevered,* had thrown himself totally into the fires of the new life, the mystic path. *He* had done no such thing. He had settled for sobriety, for freedom from alcoholism. Had there been someone then to instruct and guide him, he might have done the same, but the fact was, he had not. And now, glad he had not. St. Paul had his mission, and he had his, which was to establish and safeguard the sobriety of thousands, and tens of thousands, and soon the hundreds of thousands of alcoholics and the happiness of all their families as well. One had pursued saintliness, the other sobriety, and each had done his duty, accomplished his tasks.

He could not have it both ways. The potency in Chris' appeal was undeniable but he would not allow it to sway him from the conviction that if he had it to do all over again he would act as he had.

There was one other important way they had differed. Paul's mystical experience had undoubtedly been much stronger than his own. It had blinded him for three days and literally *drove* him—until spiritual clarity and understanding had been attained—into the Arabian solitudes for those three years. And it had forced out of him—though much later, no doubt—such an extreme teaching as *pray without ceasing,* which must have meant—*had* to have meant—that prayer every moment was for him *necessary,* since the experience on the Damascus Road had penetrated his psyche at so deep a level that thereafter his whole existence *every moment* was precariously balanced on a knife-edge of dependence on the divine being not only for grace to feed his new spirituality but to keep him sane—perhaps even to stay alive.

Thus for Paul, prayer was not a beautiful spiritual adornment to his life but *was* his life. For such a man, to cease praying even for a moment—apparently—meant that he was subject to the return of the negative and destructive forces that must have been his daily experience prior to Damascus. In all of this one saw the sudden emergence of the mystic and saint in embryo—no one else could have conceived the necessity of so startling a pronouncement as *pray without ceasing.*

With himself it was very different.

He had come to see that the power and intensity of his own awakening had been just enough—and no more—for him to bear. He had brought to it a mind unleavened by any kind of genuine prayer or spiritual activity—not to speak of the ravaged body: brain and tissue and constitution half-ruined by his derelict years—and thus would have been able to withstand the sudden influx of only a small degree of pure light, absolute consciousness. His nervous system would have been shattered otherwise.

In short, he had been too frail and shoddy a container to have received more than a modicum of divine grace. His background of emotional violence, self-indulgence so long protracted, raw egoism, obsession, and despair, had all been too recent not to have rendered him unfit for more grace than was necessary.

It was, to speak truly, not an experience of the mountain so much as of the foothills.

Enough to awaken him, not enough to transform.

Just a little had come to him—what he could manage—but it had been enough to save him, to free him, and to give birth to the miracle that was AA. It had seemed like everything to him then, because there was so much darkness in the psyche receiving the grace. To a mind so darkened and damaged a single ray of light had seemed like the sun of a new world.

Fifteen years ago....

Since then his health had returned, his whole mental and physical system rehabilitated, even apart from the draining effect of the last five years.

Now he would be able to endure a much more potent spiritual encounter if one was ever to come.

Why then was it not occurring?

The key was that he was *humbler* that time in Towns, or at least because of the urgency of his need he had been able—sufficient for the time—to *achieve* humility. *Now* ... his mind, once so expressive and creative, was cluttered with shadows passing for reality. He was no longer so simple as he had been then *and no longer able* to reach that necessary degree of humility—the need, the naked turning to the Higher Power for help, the active, real sense of *abandonment.*

He had believed then that he was going to die or go mad, but he did not at bottom really believe that now. The depression was sabotaging his life but did not seem actually to be killing him.

Though in fact it was.

Nevertheless somehow he thought he could survive this present impasse *sooner or later* ... and so could not summon up that extra reserve of intensity and single-mindedness needed before the grace could be felt. The ego, during that night at Towns, had been *displaced,* dislodged from its usual role of dominance in his psychic life—erased at least fleetingly. But during those precious moments the contact, deep within, had been made, the mysterious merging of all the parts of his being for just a few transforming seconds, the one moment of truth he had genuinely known.

Now the ego was not only palpably present but was, as he had come to believe, taking the very form of the depression itself.

Now, also, because of his achievement with AA he was *engulfed with pride.* Despite his despondencies and self-reproach, he could hear at every moment a voice within reminding him of his unique position in the modern world, of his triumphant success—attaining a victory of such a kind that few men in history could equal.

It was different now. Quite different!

He was light years away from a return of the experience. As you sow, so shall you reap. He had neglected it when he had it, had failed to appreciate it (for what seemed sufficient cause) while it was with him, and now he was reaping what he had sown.

Wreck of humanity though he was that night fifteen years ago, he was—spiritually—far closer to the truth, to the Real, to the divine, than present, fettered in the iron death-grip of self-infatuated egoism and unable—totally unable, it appeared—to generate the saving measure of humility that would vault him out of the torpor that was his life.

And the will ... to *want* to do so.

There was another crucial point of comparison. Paul had described his vision as emanating from without. *There shone round about him a light from heaven ... and he heard a voice saying....* As he himself had at first thought, the way anyone suddenly caught up in such an encounter *would* have. As he later wrote: "—A great wind, not of air, but of spirit, blew ... I felt possessed by an absolute power—"

The light had come *from within,* the sense of power, of being possessed, the sensation of a great wind blowing through him—all from within. Paul too would inevitably have had to come to the same conclusion. So many phrases in his epistles seemed charged with a significance quite different than he gave to the original description on the road to Damascus: *Christ in you the hope of glory, In him we live and move and have our being.* All identifying him as a genuine seer, as Chris Eastman had pointed out in his comments on Paul's spiritual development ... "from a once-born hounder of Christians to a true mystic...."

Yes, now he knew the truth. And there was painful irony in the fact that this insight into the source of revelation had been the fruit of these last five sick, brooding years.

The treasure that had appeared to him that night in Towns was still there, still with him, sleeping and inaccessible within the massive indolence that was his mind.

Life was within him, as was death. Spirituality, along with egoism. Perhaps everything in its essence was there, along with a powerful obstruction to his ever *realizing* the truth.

What *was* he? What was man? *Truly...?*

14 A Passion to Know

Suddenly released by that moment in Towns, a world of untapped
energies sprang into being and for the next five months powered
an intense, crowded chapter of his life. And all of it *sober*, his sobriety
seeming to deepen day by day.

Ebby Thatcher took pride in the transformation, making himself
at home at Clinton Street much of the time, living there for various
periods, and of course in attendance with Lois and himself at the
Oxford Group meetings held during the week at Sam Shoemaker's
Calvary Episcopal Church on East Twenty-first Street.

He could not get enough of the meetings and would have gone
every night if he could, for out of them and their spiritual philosophy
of repentance and submission to the indwelling God had come, through
Ebby, the lead into his own rebirth.

Lois was in thrall to an ambivalence of motive after his Towns
experience. At first there was joy, incredulity, ecstatic happiness for
him, for both of them. But she did not feel needed now, since obviously
he had done on his own—with the help of the Oxford Group teachings,
the example of Ebby, and the grace of God—what she with her
thousands of prayers and acts of forbearance and sacrifice had been
unable to do.

Further, on the strength of her moral upbringing and the
tendencies of her own ethical, God-fearing nature she had always rested

in the conviction that she understood what religion was and thus stood in no special need of the Oxford Group and what it was communicating of higher values to those who did need it. She accompanied Bill at first quite willingly and enthusiastically, since *he* was obviously deriving such benefit from them, but gradually after a few months a reaction appeared.

One night they were late getting ready in their Brooklyn house for the subway ride to Manhattan and somewhat impatiently he had urged her to hurry. She responded by hurling a shoe at him.

"Hurry, my foot!" she exclaimed. "You and your old meetings! You're making a religion out of them!"

Enjoying a rare moment of detachment in their relationship, he stooped down, picked up the rejected shoe, and imperturbably returned it to her. Even as he did so, he reflected that such outbursts were possible for a nonalcoholic who was also a once-born soul: someone, as he was beginning to understand such things, who had not felt the grace of God *directly* in her being. But they were a luxury he could not safely indulge any more himself, both as an alcoholic and as a twice-born entity who *had* received that grace and who, therefore, on two counts was *compelled* to live well: as an alcoholic and as one whose soul had been opened to the gaze of the divine.

He had lived a wretched life for more than a decade but, sinner or not, there was no doubt that now he was a prisoner of the Divine Power behind everything and of the lifestyle that made for the reinforcement of his sobriety.

Such concepts and shifting states of mind were made more real for him by his continued reading of James' classic, which had become like a second Bible for him during these months.

But his principal activity, his full-time employment, though he did it without compensation, was working with alcoholics in all stages of addiction. Fed in secret by the lingering power of the Towns theophany, strengthened by the ideas and personalities he encountered at the Calvary meetings of the Oxford Group, and liberated by the wonder-filled days of his new sobriety, he sought out still suffering victims with a unique passion—went after them like a hunter after his prey.

In his imagination he saw himself presiding over a vast and spreading empire of recovered addicts saved by his efforts and inspired by his example.

He wanted them, however, to follow *his* pattern, to recover via the stages *he* had gone through. But none—irrationally enough—chose to emulate him, none understood what he was talking about when he spoke of the great light of peace and blessedness waiting to fall upon the head of the man truly repentant, genuinely surrendered.

Still he carried on, day and night seeking them out at the Calvary Mission near the Church on East Twenty-third Street and at Towns too, where he operated with a private carte blanche from Dr. Silkworth, pouncing on dried-out patients before they were able to leave and freely bringing many of his prospects to Clinton Street for special one-to-one rehabilitation: succeeding, after nearly five months of this activity, with not a single one.

In his passionate proselytizing only one person had been helped: *himself.* In the urgency of trying to reach the mind of each prospective convert, he forgot his own problems, his unemployment, his ruined reputation on Wall Street, forgot himself totally.

Despite Lois' recurrent conflicts over his unbroken attendance at the Oxford meetings, she was a model of cooperation towards the plan of accepting still active drinkers at their Clinton Street home.

It did not bother him unduly that he was failing with each targeted individual, failing to communicate, apparently to any of them, the significance and scope of what had happened to *him.* For something unusual was occurring: he always felt not only better after these futile encounters but his sobriety mysteriously deepened.

Dr. Silkworth one day urged him to change his tactics, from preaching "religion" at men in the least likely condition to respond to a religious message, to emphasizing the *illness*-aspect of alcoholism.

"Tell them they have an allergy, an obsession, a disease," the little, white-thatched doctor stressed. "Show them how *hopeless* they are. *Then* give them the religion."

He did this, but with no better results. He did not mind. He continued tirelessly as before, it had become his ruling passion, and every one acquainted with him knew it.

The members of the Shoemaker Oxford Group certainly did, and though they tolerated what he was doing, they were none too enthusiastic about it. They thought that, recovered alcoholic or not, he should not concentrate his efforts in so narrow a field. He should draw no distinctions—all men needed spiritual salvation, and alcoholics could claim no special dispensation. Besides, alcoholics, when shown a welcoming door in the past, had proved unreliable, even untrustworthy, had been known to act in highly unpredictable ways.

They also might have added that their collective experience over many years had revealed alcoholics to be the least promising group of sinners they had had to deal with and by now they had all but written them off as prospects for spiritual therapy. That is why they found his unabated passion on their behalf so distressing.

But he knew that in time he could understand them as no nonalcoholic could hope to do, speak their language, read their minds, anticipate their rationalizations, establish a bond which might be the key to their conversion.

So he continued with his efforts as before, despite his failure to get them to listen whether he spoke about the disease or the spiritual factor. He was in no hurry. He would give himself time. He would persist, experimenting, learning, never show impatience, would pray for them too—*his* people, *his* sinners.

He was untroubled that Ebby Thatcher felt no comparable urge to work with victims of alcoholism but seemed satisfied that his visit to Clinton Street that day in November had been sufficient. His gratitude to Ebby for having appeared when he had was so strong and persistent that it never occurred to him to stand in judgment on Ebby's hands-off approach and his preference for the more genteel milieu of the Oxford Group meetings, where he struck the nonalcoholic members as a shining example of what Bill Wilson should be.

He could not agree with them more about Ebby.

During this whole period, as well as later, he instinctively deferred to Ebby as the "man who got me sober," and that is how the alcoholics who gathered with him in the Twenty-third Street cafeteria near the

Calvary Mission, and at Clinton Street, came to think of him. In the process he neutralized the potential of his ego, which, he well knew, was uncomfortable with gratitude for anything, especially one's life.

During one of their rare private times in this period Lois took the opportunity to share her thoughts about the continued resistance he was meeting among drinkers, even among those who appeared to want to get sober.

"... Bill, you're onto something. I don't know what it is and I don't think you do, but there is something mysterious and revolutionary here and if we wait long enough and if you can be patient we're bound to discover what it is. We have to remember that all important new undertakings face periods of adversity and discouragement at the beginning. The time of testing cannot be bypassed or escaped, Bill."

She had touched the very nerve of his own thinking on the subject, though he had been hesitant about announcing it.

"I think I have a message for them if I can just find the right way to bring it forth and find out also what the message actually is!"

She gazed at him, her dark eyes full of love and admiration.

"*You* are the message, Bill...."

Remaining silent, moved by her faith and her words, he thought: It was true. If it could happen to him, then to anyone.

But one mid-morning in April, at Clinton Street, in an empty house (a rare occurrence now), a sudden desire for alcohol seized him. Swift and instant the craving had come, like a lightning-flash in a dark summer sky. It lacked the dominating power of so many he had known, but it was enough to humiliate and terrify him.

Until then he had begun to wonder, as the weeks of sobriety passed into months, if he was still an alcoholic—or *as much* as he had once been. Oxford Group members had spoken to him as though he no longer was:

"You and Ebby are different from those you're working with, Bill—that's obvious. We know you've had a drinking history, but that's all behind you. You've been changed by the grace of God!"

Yes, he had wondered. Now he knew. He *was* still an alcoholic, and "just as much" so as ever. The craving that filled him, though manageable, was not unlike many he had weathered in the past and if he yielded to it he knew the result would be the same. No, not the same—*worse*. Uncannily, as he had earlier discovered, the disease progressed even if you were not drinking. The experience of those he had been working with tallied all too closely with his own.

As he stood in the middle of the kitchen, immobilized by conflicting desires, a new thought, as sudden as the craving—freeing him, distancing him from the crisis—possessed him. If he didn't take a drink—the first drink of many—he could not get drunk. He walked to his bedroom, procured from its locked drawer his new journal-book, gripped with the feeling of a special, perhaps a historic moment come to pass.

Very deliberately he wrote: "It's the first drink that gets you drunk."

And then another thought began to form, breaking in on the first....

He had been assuming that they needed him and his message: confess your powerlessness, admit your life is a wreck, deflate yourself at depth, turn to the higher power for help with total concentration, let the light break, let the grace flow ... a message that had helped no one—except himself!

The other part of the message was not so much that they needed him as that *he needed them.* Suddenly, with tidal power, the thought of his prospects in New York waiting for him—he also waiting for *them!*— steadied and sobered him. The desire ebbed, he could feel it moment by moment weakening. With a mild, confident effort he turned away from it and, still shaking in the aftermath of his victory (his first such), he headed out the door like a warrior well-trained for the battle life has shaped him for.

Just prior to this he had begun the diary-notebook, the beginning of what would become his secret journal, to be carefully preserved over the years under lock and key, now secure in the drawer of his studio desk. He thought of it as the first draft of a huge volume of alcoholic wisdom that would establish him as the world's foremost authority.

At last he could genuinely become Number One in something. And in what better field to excel?

Hitherto he had never thought of himself as a writer; all at once he found the idea compelling—the most natural thing to do.

His complete failure in converting alcoholics to his message may really have meant that he was destined to be a *thinker,* not a proselytizer!

A great contemplative analyst of the whole terrain of alcoholism and of its victims. The man everyone would come to for answers on this vexed subject.

At first he wrote about his experience with individual addicts, but gradually, as his skill in expression improved, he began to address himself to ideas and principles behind the encounters.

"I feel on the verge of some great realization" had been his opening line.

His mind groped for knowledge of itself, for the meaning of his experiences, for the truth of alcoholism—for some reality (which Lois too had intuited) eluding him like a shadow.

Even as he sat down to his writing table at midnight he felt in the hands of destiny. He had assumed the mantle and psychology of an author almost at once—as though born to it.

Perhaps, without having known it before, he *was.*

Amazingly he had discovered that, despite the years of insane addiction and despite what Dr. Silkworth and others had said, his brain had *not* been damaged. He was certain it was as good as ever— in a sense better! Under the burdens of thought he was now imposing on it, it had proved to be clear and forceful, often brilliant.

A new dream had appeared: he would become a great writer. Out of the chaos of his past, a literary genius may have been born.

Why was it, he wondered, and promptly pursued the idea in the journal, that despite his unbroken lack of success with alcoholic victims, he did not feel in any way disheartened? On the contrary, he always felt *better*—stronger, freer, rejuvenated—after his daily wrestling with their problems, as they called them—though in fact they had only one problem. (In solving that, what else could they *not* solve?)

What was the answer?

Venerable phrases like *virtue is its own reward* sprang to his mind as help in coming to grips with the challenge, and he thought that very likely that was the principle behind it: namely, a virtuous action, a good work, a responsibility discharged, if undertaken for its own sake and not for the gain it might bring, was truly its own reward, and fulfillment.

And he was able to throw himself into his work and do it for its own sake without any thought of reward because he was able to completely identify with the men he sought out and struggled with so tenaciously. Just the chance to work with them, *be* with them, *sharing himself* with them, was all the reward he had needed.

And the result was the sense of liberation, strength, and well-being—*and freedom from the desire to drink alcohol*—that possessed him every time.

In serving and helping others you helped yourself! That was the discovery he still found difficult to assimilate. In forgetting himself he found *another* self, a greater self than he had been, or had known. And, thanks to his commitment to others, growing stronger every day.

Unexpectedly a new idea: Could someone gain this strength without the awakening that he had experienced—without religion, without God?

The essential was service, help, dedication, losing yourself in the desire to do something for others. Such a way of life freed you from the ego—at least from its worst ravages—and you felt a new identity rushing in to fill the vacuum caused by your self-forgetfulness.

But the thought continued to hound him: what was the role of religion in this? It appeared that religion was not actually necessary, though it could provide an impetus at the outset. *Belief in God was not essential.* Belief helped, made it easier for you to act, to serve, *to be*. But it was action—selfless action—that changed you.

Action, not belief. An atheist could realize God if he acted well enough—with sufficient purity of motive. After all, it had happened to *him*. He would not be speaking from hearsay. His prayer in Towns had not been that of a believing man but of an *un*-believing one, an atheist. He had gone into the experience without belief, had come out of it a believer in God.

Faith and belief provided direction, incentive, and power but only
if accompanied by action. The *deed* saved us, for it changed us *and in
the change we were saved*. Not to be saved meant we did not change.

Selfless action, selfless commitment—that was the way, the secret.
Given to *him*.

His mind was almost bursting with its new knowledge.

Yes—action, not belief.

He had had *both* working for him, but not everyone might be so
fortunate. The Towns experience had made him strong in one way,
the missionary work—for that is how he thought of it—strong in
another. Both seemed vital, both had been vital to him. But of the two
it was the work, the service, the losing of oneself in the commitment,
that was indispensable.

In time a greater spiritual experience might reveal a whole different
picture but for the present the facts as he had pondered them were
clear and unmistakable enough.

He tried to bury these insights into the depths of his mind, using
his journal as an aid in helping to assimilate them.

Once more he went over the whole thing, consciously trying to
impress upon his mind the importance of the subject and the significance of his illumination, and to make sure he was not deluding
himself:

A *law,* no less, was at work here—some hidden spiritual law, of
which he had heard but had not yet discovered, and hence for him
had had no real meaning—a universal principle, a law of moral
causation whose operation made you strong if you acted one way,
weak if in another.

Religion—once again? Its role?

Religion followed after.

The law was timeless, ageless, whereas even the greatest religions
had begun at some point in time.

And therefore would end at some point in time?

So it seemed. Whatever had begun, he had read somewhere, would
inevitably have to end.

But this law, like the other laws of nature—laws of God, he
preferred to think of them—were apart from time, space, and causation.

They were coexistent with the universe, with the mind of God: eternal in their nature, operation, and purpose. Long after they had been observed, religion began, coming as a help to man to enable him to obey them, including this one he had made his own discovery, though it was one all great thinkers and sages had known and spoken of: the law of karma, of sowing and reaping...

Something was goading him to store this law and his understanding of it deep in his mind, never to be lost, as though he might have some acute need for it at some unforeseeable hour more threatening than the moment of temptation he had survived in April.

15 Akron

During this same period he began to worry about his prolonged unemployment. He knew that people were talking. The Oxford Group members, for instance. They noted his return to health, his new color, his brighter eye, his increasing confidence. They wondered. He could better spend his time with a regular job than with his numerous alcoholic friends. He grew uneasy and began once more to send out inquiries in Wall Street. But he had broken too many promises to too many people. One answered favorably. The rest were silent.

With Lois it was a different story. She did not wonder, did not count the days when he should return to work. As with the strangers, dry or half-drunk, who camped in her living room at all hours, she was uncomplaining. Remembering the horrors of not too distant a time, she was content.

Indeed when he did find employment with the single contact who had responded to his letters, she was alarmed, for the position would take him to Akron, Ohio for an indeterminate period—away from her and the way of life he had been pursuing with such ardor and happiness. The suddenness of the offer made her anxious, tense. Alone in a strange city—how would he fare? Intuitive fears seized her, though she was careful to conceal her apprehension lest he think she had little faith in his sobriety.

Her mood recalled the agonizing nights she had lived through for so many years.

He himself did not think along these lines. He saw the situation only as a chance to restore his name in the financial world and once again become a profitable wage earner. So passionately did he feel about the opportunity that it did not occur to him that in throwing himself into the assignment with the commitment it required he would be turning away from the alcoholic work that had been stabilizing him.

Hence he missed the ominous dimension lurking in this latest development.

The challenge had been offered by an old Wall Street colleague, Howard Tompkins, who wrote to tell him how impressed he had been by his apparently total rehabilitation—as far as Bill knew, the only one who had been.

Tompkins and his New York supporters had collected a number of shares in a floundering machine-tool company in Akron and by acquiring as many proxies as possible in and around Akron were planning to out-vote a competing block for control of the company at the annual stockholders meeting early in May. Besides Tompkins and his group and the rival Wall Street firm, which likewise had just sent representatives to fight for it in Akron, there was the discredited management.

Tompkins felt that Bill would be just the one to assist the three associates he was about to dispatch to Akron to organize their takeover bid. Was he willing to go? One of the inducements in offering him the job was the chance to become an officer of the reorganized company.

He gave his answer with little delay. He *was* willing to go ... and privately, as he warmed to the task, he nurtured visions of himself as company president, gradually taking control from Tompkins himself, but somehow doing it in such a manner that everyone would feel benefited.

That he was able to indulge such fantasies so quickly after turning away from the work at Towns and Calvary Mission demonstrated the potential danger of his position—a thought that never occurred to him.

After he had won Lois' support (though her misgivings remained) he promised to phone her regularly and, if all went according to Tompkins' schedule for victory, to be back by the middle of May.

In Akron it did not take long to discover that the opposition camp had persuaded management to join forces with it against the Tompkins team (one of whom, they declared, was a notorious alcoholic whose influence would destroy the company), with the result that despite their best efforts Bill and his partners failed to win a majority of the proxies at the stockholders meeting. After which, the Tompkins men spent little time before setting out again for New York, leaving Bill behind to continue the battle, perhaps to investigate with legal help the possibility that fraud had been perpetrated. They promised to send necessary funds, then left him alone in the Mayflower hotel, the room paid for over the next few days. He had ten dollars in his pocket.

He was deflated. Seemingly on the threshold of a victory that would mean so much to his future and to a more comfortable life for Lois, he was in effect abandoned by allies, left to his own devices at the beginning of a warm, spring weekend in an unfamiliar city.

The next scene always remained in his memory in a light of permanence, a moment in its consequences equal in importance to the Towns' enlightenment, indeed the culmination of the earlier grace ... just as the Akron interlude in the proxy fight, which seemed superficially cut off from what he had been doing, was in reality its fulfillment.

The New Yorkers had hardly left him in his room when the desire to drink returned like a blanketing cloud, filling him, a sudden devouring thirst not so much for alcohol as for what it could bring: release, renewal, *otherness* from what had seized him.

He stood in the middle of the hotel room like a scarecrow swept by tumultuous winds in a cornfield. He felt assaulted by his own mind, skewered by blind hot thrusts of desire.

It was much worse than that time last month in Brooklyn. Then he had been close to a great many people, any one of whom he might have called as a last resort. There he had been surrounded by reminders of sobriety and of the work he was doing with alcoholics. Here there was no one. In the whole of Akron he knew not a soul, and his immediate environment was the seductive impersonality of a large modern hotel whose very disinterestedness invited to transgressions that would not be noticed.

As well, the previous urge to drink had seemed in retrospect more symbolic than real, an overdue test of the depth of his sobriety and easily enough controlled. *Now* it was a tangible frightening thing with nothing symbolic about it at all.

His mind churned wildly in its two-sided conflict. An inner voice warned him: he must quickly, without delay, recapture a sense of the known and familiar to shore up his strength ... to give him a sense of *connection*.

But how? Something was missing ... but what?

Desperately the voice of his hard-won sobriety, of sanity itself, struggled to prevail as he wavered irresolutely. Even as the contest proceeded, his will now leaning this way, now that, his feet—obeying their own authority—had taken him to the elevator and thence to the hotel lobby and an inconspicuous armchair in a corner where he could continue his deliberations, his eye on the bar that opened conveniently onto the lobby, his ears nostalgically embracing the murmur of muted voices, the tinkle of ice against glasses, the congenial sound of music from the bar radio ... producing an emanation of quiet joy, camaraderie, a sense of mutual acceptance, even of conspiracy—like that day long ago with Mark Whalon in the Marble Man tavern, and the first opening glimpse into another world.

That is what he wanted and needed, not the alcohol, not the drunkenness certainly, not the wild abandon. *That* was his objective, and never more prized than when, as now, he least possessed it.

He got up from the armchair and looked toward the bar, the door left invitingly open. With five full months of sobriety, the most he had achieved since his first drink, was it likely he was the same man who had *stumbled* into Towns those times? Was it not *more* likely that he was *changed*, more seasoned than ever, healthier surely, more *aware*?

Warning voices thronged his memory ... Lois ("If you could see what you look like when you drink, you would never drink again"),

Dr. Silkworth ("Stress the disease angle, show them they're dead if they in-take alcohol in any form"), Ebby ("I don't need to drink any more, Bill")...

But all he wanted was one, perhaps two drinks, or perhaps a single cold beer and that would be the end. Had he learned nothing in those five months? Another voice: "How *winning* you look, Lieutenant!"

He would take the drink in honor of Mother's Day tomorrow.

He started tentatively toward the open door, but a strange leadenness had seized him, weighting his feet and legs; he felt suddenly *heavy,* slow, alien to himself, felt his body being *compressed* by some outside force shaking and squeezing him like a huge fist. He stopped, stood uncertainly in the middle of the lobby, his thoughts in turmoil.

A great fear had possessed him, a memory of terror. He felt immobile, incapable of moving.

That time last month in Brooklyn—almost drinking... what was different then?

The experience with alcoholics! The exhilaration it had given him, the sense of *strength,* the wholeness. He had needed *them.* That was the difference. And needed them now! But he knew no one in all of Akron...

A vagrant, capricious thought arose: *A-kron* ... meaning *no time*—timeless ... and the mood upon him like that—timeless, dream-like.

He looked wildly toward the other end of the lobby—a phone booth. Near it a church directory. As he stood hesitating, the lobby seemed charged with a peculiar energy, a ray of power shimmering in the atmosphere, like nothing he had known.

He faltered toward the directory, began by calling a minister, randomly chosen, who gave him more numbers to call, desperately dialing, the fear still dogging him, still sapping his will, but not so strong now. Something else had supervened.

Mayflower, he thought ... the pilgrim ship that had set out for a new world. He felt like the captain on the bridge in a fateful storm, his phone calls like SOS messages at an eleventh hour sent out to other ships passing in the night.

"... Hello, hello,...."

Finally succeeding in reaching someone who grasped what he was talking about, and a local Oxford Group member at that, who referred him to another member, Henrietta Seiberling. The calls had changed everything. He did not know just how but they had—those cries for help to anyone out there who might be listening.

Perhaps merely the *willingness* to be sober, to be helped, the willingness to *seek* help was enough to turn the mind in a new direction and free it from the cloud of darkness that had covered it.

Whatever the reason, he knew he felt different. Not completely out of harm's way, but safer, stronger. Almost sober again.

Contact was made with Henrietta Seiberling. He was to go immediately to her address and meet a physician named Dr. Robert Smith, an alcoholic who had systematically succeeded in destroying his practice, but as it turned out he was just then, they learned, near the end of a strenuous drinking bout and would not be available until five on Sunday, more than twenty-four long hours distant.

How to get through that time safely?

He was still in danger, that he knew, though the desire had ebbed considerably, and reason, his higher will perhaps, had rushed in to steady him with reminding admonitions.

It's the first drink that gets you drunk.

He had embraced that principle fervently already. But it was not the whole truth, not enough of the truth, which was:

It was alcoholic *thinking* that got you drunk.

With his thoughts more coherent and moving more slowly than before he made the call, he felt more secure. *Mind* was the temptation, not the alcohol. A settled, positive mind was the protection, not so much the absence of alcohol.

How to last through that period?

He would be all right, he was sure of it now. The kinds of thoughts he was having were signs of control, sanity, stability—that fact reassured him.

But he would do whatever he could to help himself... like passing the time in ways that would increase his strength, give him a greater margin of safety—such as leaving most of his money in the room while he went down to the coffee shop for a slow, carefully eaten meal away from the sounds coming from the bar. And after that? He would think of something, he felt carried forward on a wave of inspiration that would take him where he wanted to go.

Why not a movie after the meal, a time-consuming double-feature? There were several theaters in this part of town, anyone of which would be satisfactory. And then a long, tiring walk for miles and miles, with the rest of his money left in the room. Returning, he would be exhausted, ready for sleep.

All of which, he recalled, he had done, with predictably positive results, including the restorative sleep of many hours, waking late, getting out of bed at noon, followed by a bracing shower and a few exercises and then something to eat at the coffee shop again. Afterwards he lingered over the Sunday paper. Combined with prayers of thanksgiving for the release that had come was a sense of victory, the mood of self-mastery ... so that he was not sorry now that the desire to drink had risen yesterday, even as strong as it had been, for in combating it there had followed this consciousness of victory—*over himself.*

Which he would not have experienced had not the struggle been so desperate. Without the temptation there would have been no conquest. Without the enemy to fight against there would have been no rediscovery of what and who he really was. Without the evil no good would have been known.

Yes, mind was not only the temptation it was the liberator. By making contact with the higher centers he had liberated himself from the fear of drinking and had remade himself into a new image.

Could he do this more and more until he had truly accomplished what he yearned to be?

At least he would go to the imminent meeting with Dr. Smith—already thinking of him as Dr. Bob—with a serene power that might make him more successful with this man than he had been with so many in New York. For one thing, he would go knowing that whether or not Dr. Bob needed him, *he needed Dr. Bob.*

With all that had happened since he left for Akron, he had an auspicious feeling, almost a conviction, that this time he would be able to impart the message and find it had reached its target.

And if he could, if the two of them could realize what had happened, or what *might* happen, then—*

His thoughts swirled, his breath came in irregular patterns, as a peculiar kind of excitement possessed him, filling him with intuitions he had never had—consciously, at least.

He regretted he had not brought his journal book with him from Brooklyn, for these were the trains of thought that ought to be recorded in all their freshness and vitality. Or at least—until he was back at Clinton Street—to be carefully savored, despite their strangeness and tentative nature, by brooding over them now, hatching them, letting them carry him onwards to possibilities like a dream, a more exciting dream than his fantasies, one so vast, so grand, that he felt awestruck by the power of his imagination.

But it was not only imagination. It felt like reality. Like the shape of his future.

---

* The historic meeting between Bill W. and Dr. Bob, which marked the beginning of AA, took place at the appointed time on Mother's Day, Sunday May 12, 1935. Dr. Bob said the reason Bill was able to help him stay sober was that, "He talked my language"—Bill knew from experience what Dr. Bob had gone through.

PART THREE

16 The Omen

After Akron, the fruit of Towns, there was no return to what had been. A new era dawned, almost tangible in its effect, giving him again—more focused than ever—the feeling of being in the hands of destiny. Everything he had lived through seemed now a prelude to the main drama, which had begun not in Manhattan but in the unlikeliest of places.

As he looked back to the post-Akron period, he startled himself with the question: Was AA the result of his dreams, the projection of his own inner life appearing in simply another form? Was it a drama he had called into being by the passion of his need, by his power of imagination?

And was his depression, now become his way of life, the result of his failure to manage such portentous questions? Was it self-will in another form—the AA movement a tribute to that potentiality in a unique way, the depression in still another?

In his journal he asked: "Am I some kind of incognito yogi with the power of mind to create worlds, to inhabit lives by the thousand, to generate out of my own needs and longings a universe—the one in fact I dwell in?"

And, again—was his depression an instinctive manifestation of this awesome insight—and his inability to cope with it?

Who *was* he?

Great as AA now was, he felt himself still greater, as a parent feels greater than his offspring. Was it not his own life that had been given to *them,* his own ideas become their program, his own writings their literature? Was not his own hand on every aspect of AA? Was not *he himself* AA in all essentials?

For a long time after the seminal Akron meeting with Dr. Bob AA was nameless, befitting its slow growth in both New York and Akron, whither he frequently returned after his initial stay of three months with Dr. Bob and his wife Anne on Ardmore Avenue. It was essentially a secret society. After more than three years, while he was putting together the Big Book, they could count only a hundred recovered cases, by far the greater number of these centered in Akron and, gradually, in Cleveland.

As before, he had difficulty—though no longer total failure—in his efforts to convert other prospects. But at least his first success was the one that counted: Dr. Bob himself... notably effective with active alcoholics in Akron, choosing a simple, take-it-or-leave-it approach and shaming them into sobriety, forcing them to capitulate there before him in the hospital ward, or wherever the confrontation took place; otherwise threatening to have nothing more to do with them. Though most of his charges drank again, a fair number did not.

As time passed, Bill realized why his first and—until then—his only success had to be in Ohio. If it had not been, what he was doing would become known—to the degree that it became known at all—as an eastern, specifically New York-based activity and would probably have failed to take root in the rest of the country, as it did slowly, then evermore steadily, once *Alcoholics Anonymous* (referred to as the Big Book) came out in the spring of 1939, four years after the Mother's Day meeting. Even after he had made many more trips to Akron during that period, and met the new recruits, he always was aware of their Midwestern reservations about him and the artificial world of Wall Street and the "big city" while their own roots had sprung from the purer earth of Middle America.

And from the beginning their hero was Dr. Bob, not Bill Wilson with all his never-ending ideas. Down-to-earth, rough-hewn Dr. Bob, a man with a profane vocabulary who loved to drive fast cars and called his wife "the skirt."

But if that was what was required to make the new society work, so be it. That is why from the beginning he pushed the idea that Dr. Bob was a cofounder of their fledgling society, deserving of equal credit with himself. Which was fine with the Ohioans, who thought Bob knew what was best for AA anyway.

But had their wishes prevailed, theirs and Dr. Bob's, there would have been no AA, only a variation of the secret society meeting in private homes, which in fact for the first four years it had actually been. Parlor-AA, backed by a little reading of the New Testament, was their version of what for him was a movement that would cover the world, might be known from one end of the earth to the other.

Dr. Bob, in short, wanted AA to remain in future what it had been during those very early, admittedly exciting and heroic days. He wanted it to become known chiefly by word of mouth, in this way preserving intact its informal, one-on-one character, avoiding the necessity of any organization whatever.

He himself knew that AA needed its guidelines, its principles set down for all to contemplate, needed a record of its history and its struggles, needed its Big Book—as their bible came to be known. Without such literature it would be doomed to a short life: he saw this very clearly from the beginning and argued for its adoption month after month, meeting grudging opposition at every step from the dominant Ohio faction that reflected Dr. Bob's views, only barely, after all his efforts, gaining a one-vote approval of his plan to go ahead in New York (showing them periodically the fruits of his labors) with his literary campaign to make AA respectable ... and lasting.

As for the idea of Dr. Bob as cofounder, it was largely his own doing—for two distinct reasons, both kept concealed from others. First, in the early period, he wanted to solidify the bond between himself, the elitist Manhattanite, with the ever-suspicious Midwesterners: hearing him constantly praise their leader as equally important as himself mollified their suspicions and to some extent neutralized (though never as much as he hoped) their reservations.

Then later, after 1939, he kept advancing the same idea to provide
an escape if he should slip back into drinking: in which event, the
fall—he kept telling himself—would not be quite so great if there was
someone else to share the burden of leadership.

Though in fact Dr. Bob never accepted the role at any time.

Chris argued that that was because, in his fundamental honesty,
Bob knew he was no leader, rather the one picked out to be in the right
place at the right moment when the lightning struck.

"The lightning was *you*," said Chris. It was true. "Without Dr.
Bob—or *someone*—the lightning you had to offer to the world would
have been short-circuited. To that extent he was necessary, though
how many others might have served as well?"

He reminded Chris of the roles the Oxford Group and James'
Varieties had played in the formulation of the ideas he bequeathed to
AA.

"But how many did the Oxford Group or William James get
sober?" Chris asked.

From his studio, years after the fact, even seeing AA itself as only
a reflex of his own psychic life, he knew that Dr. Bob was as Chris
described him: not a man to be cofounder of something like AA, not
a visionary, not a man to receive transcendental insight, *not a prophet
type,* for all his value and influence in other respects, especially in the
very early days when they were both flying blind.

Indeed there was, he knew now, no cofounder. Great ideas visited
the minds of individuals, not partnerships. The solitary mind was the
shrine of truth. Organization (even such as there was of it in AA), the
give-and-take of committee work, and the like, came later, but had
little to do with the original revelation.

With writing more and more his passion, taking over his life, he
began to set down his thoughts on AA and its guiding principles, and
when it came time to write the Big Book in earnest, his mind had
already mastered the territory he had to traverse. He well remembered
the day in Clinton Street when, in his upstairs bedroom, feeling rather
poorly just then, a sudden inspiration descended upon him and in a
matter of a few minutes—less than an hour at most—he had written

down the Twelve Steps for inclusion in the Big Book, to be revised only minimally.

By now they were carved in stone. Even he could not change them at this date, though there were a few places where his alcoholic thinking—undetected by others in the grip of the same outlook—was too much in evidence.

The sixth step, for example—*Were entirely ready to have God remove all these defects of character*—where the narcissism of the alcoholic character was evident. Were entirely ready to be made pure and perfect? Who, in truth, not alcoholics alone, *really* could make that prayer—and mean it?

Not himself.

It was like the prayer of Augustine: Make me chaste, O Lord—but later, not now!

And the twelfth step: *Having had a spiritual awakening as the result of these steps*—how presumptuous. As though life's greatest boon, a "spiritual awakening" (with all that implied) could be *scheduled,* brought about by merely human processes ... thus invading the unique prerogative of the divine, which alone could bring about such awakening.

Yes, he would like to make changes, but most were not possible now ... except where he could incorporate them in the new book he was intermittently working on, his in-depth analysis of both the twelve steps and the twelve traditions.

Writing the Big Book—apart from selected life histories of the first One Hundred (most of course from Ohio)—had been an exhilarating experience. From the first he had had to employ all the tact at his command to deflect members of the New York circle from making a committee kind of composition. The same tone and style had to prevail throughout, and miraculously—as others confirmed—his own was just what the work needed.

There was a brief tension with Lois when it came time to write "To Wives" and "The Family Afterwards." She had assumed she would be the one to write those sections, but her own literary style—not that of a writer or a thinker—was singularly different from his, and it was only after he had made this crystal clear that she accepted his decision.

Once the Big Book was out, there was a marked though not a radical change in the growth of the fellowship. Favorable reviews from influential individuals, radio broadcasts, articles in magazines and newspapers here and there over the next two years, brought in some sixty to seventy new members a month. Two full years after publication, membership in the spring of 1941 stood at two thousand—no longer an unknown movement but not exactly a household name: it was clear that the overwhelming majority of Americans still had not heard of AA.

With Jack Alexander's *Saturday Evening Post* article that March, everything changed forever—and he with it.

In the nine months following the article, new members tumbled into the New York office at the rate of nearly a thousand a month, bringing unmistakable signs that an exponential growth was now a possibility, with each member across the country (and abroad) tending to become a missionary for several *other* members, and so on indefinitely. There was no end in sight. The New York office was flooded with inquiries of all kinds, and on his shoulders lay the burden of dealing with the new reality—as letter-writer (dictating hundreds of letters every week), as national arbiter of disputes, as acknowledged spokesman for AA principles.

At first the thought of this mushrooming membership was exciting and bracing. It was what he and the circle around him had worked and prayed for. But gradually as that watershed year advanced he began to suffer a sense of oppression—not because of all the work heaped on him, for his energies had always been large enough for any challenge hitherto, and his power to work when it interested him was always more than sufficient for the task at hand. It was something else.

The discovery that not only would AA succeed but was likely to spread in ways and on a scale he had never guessed—at that very moment he was plunged into a serious depression which, because it lasted only a month, he was able to conceal from almost everybody except himself.

But it was real and disturbing enough, a dark omen of the blight upon him now.

The nature of AA's potentially unlimited capacity to grow beyond his wildest estimates provided him with the first indication of the close, almost intestinal relationship between AA and himself—with the bond likely to become ever more intimate.

Why, then, he asked himself, looking for a ray of light on his present condition as well—had he withdrawn for that month of January? Or for these years?

Because he could not respond to the paramount question: what was he to do now, how was he to relate to this newly awakened humanity that looked to him for answers he did not have, wisdom he did not possess, leadership he did not want to wield?

The explosion—how could it have happened so quickly?

He had tapped into some uncharted realm of human imagination, touched some hidden dimension of human nature whose consequences were incalculable, suddenly moved into a vibration of life unknown to other men.

And yet he had longed for this, dreamed of making himself irresistible to others, loved by all.

He had always lived in his dreams. His mind and imagination were his real world. The outgoing gestures and loud talking were merely the role he played, hiding the contemplative, the potential mystic. That is why he had drunk. In brooding alcoholic fantasy he had recreated the world ... little reckoning the scope and potency of his dreams, little guessing that the power of his mind, inseminated by his enormous ego, would actualize his reveries.

As if it was happening to him even now, he saw it all again....

Frightened, confused, unable to communicate, he backs off and retreats into a psychic realm of depression and anxiety, as well as of nostalgia for the self he *was*, the reality he *used* to know ... and allows this new mindset and temper of the soul to possess him: first for a month and then, not too much later, for years to come.

By the power of his dreams, fortified by an unsurpassed ego and intensely emotional nature, he had somehow, without intending to and without realizing what was under way, produced a force of mind, an acuteness of will, equal to a yogi's in its heat and concentration.

Again the thought burst like a bombshell in his mind: *had he—*

in fact, *in truth*—created AA out of the strength of his own
emotional fervor, begotten the movement out of his own imagina-
tive fires?

His mind reeled under the impact of this idea ... so esoteric, so
Oriental, at the same time so godlike, so empowering! It was the kind
of thing he might first have heard from Chris or the Princess but in
fact it had first issued from his own breast, though he had no
psychological incentive for assimilating it.

And behind it he sensed another idea, more mysterious still,
undergirding the first—namely that his self, the being that he was,
part of a universal self, was the real power, dreamer, creator of everything that came to pass in his life and his world ... and that against a
background of years of secret contemplation he had unwittingly
entered into the domain of this power.

Ideas he could speak of to no one—not to Lois, not to Chris. The
Princess would have understood, but she was gone.

He had only himself to commune with in a solitude made more
strange and trackless by this newest insight.

He did not forget that in the reaction that led him into the first
depression, ego—making use of his sobriety with the same indis-
criminate will as earlier it had made use of his addiction—was central
to the phenomenon.

It reminded him that egoism came in many guises, that it was not
always intimidating; that equally well could wear the mask of subtle
introversion, thrusting itself with neurotic obsessiveness into the
interior world with as much willfulness as it might launch its demands
on others with peremptory self-adulation. It did not always strut,
impose itself, was not always boisterous or aggressive. It could also, as
now, quietly and ruthlessly distance itself from mundane reality, could
silently refuse (for a time) to participate in a world whose manifestations it could not account for, did not understand.

Whatever its protean masks, it always represented a force that
worked against one's becoming all that one could be. It was the anti-
spiritual, self-craving element in our personality that warred every
moment on higher impulse.

In retrospect he saw this 1942 experience as a power of defeatism, ultimately of self-destruction: identifying with the inward adversary in making himself unable to endure outward success, despite his dreams ... or perhaps because of them.

17 The Princess

She appeared on the scene between the depression of early 1942 and the death-in-life that began two years later, so that during her visit he was strong and active, more or less, identifying at least adequately with the expected image of the national leader of the movement. For which he was grateful. She had come far to see him, to tell him what was on her mind, and when she had done so, after sating herself on as much AA atmosphere as possible during her stay, returned to Madras after three months unique for both of them.

Her given name, Shivani, suited her regal personality, evoking impressions of Oriental royalty, but when one of the New York members referred to her during the first days as the Princess, the name stuck, and Princess she was from then on.

Regal and commanding—but humble (in the feminine manner) also. Vulnerable to life, external and internal; sensitive to influences playing upon her spirit as an aeolian harp to the slightest breeze. Majestic and serene as a swan in one aspect of womanhood; modest, self-effacing in another. In both, magisterially chaste and aloof from the possibility of erotic blandishments: in her purity, protected like a nun in a habit.

A true woman, the most impressive he had ever met, giving him— in the fine-tuned platonic nature of their relationship during those three months—an experience of the feminine more subtle, more profound, than he had known. Deep-dyed Westerner and down-home Yankee that he was, he had to acknowledge that.

His private, long-held intuition about the truth of reincarnation seemed corroborated in her. A wealth of advancing lifetimes looked out at him through her soft, brown eyes, filled with repose. She seemed to know so much, to have lived so much!

Dressed in her Indian saris invariably, enchanting in their delicate shades of blue, green, and yellow, she dazzled him, so that when he listened to her in silence much of the time it was not because of agreement with her viewpoint necessarily as from the sense of fascination which held him in its grip.

"She's got a crush on you!" Lois exclaimed after they had met at a Manhattan group anniversary where Bill was the speaker. "She can't take her eyes off you."

He knew why. Why she had come.

She told him in their very first private meeting in her midtown hotel room. She was so filled with the passion that had propelled her a world away to meet this one man that when finally they did meet the floodgates burst open in a nonstop narrative, to which he said nothing and had no desire to say anything. Introducing it, she performed with no warning an act of ritual devotion that in a single moment, in the dramatic silence of the room overlooking Times Square on a crisp fall day, told him everything.

Approaching him in the room's one serviceable chair—she had insisted that he take it—she knelt down before him wordlessly, hands upraised in the position of prayer, eyes closed, her expression one of rapt consecration to him and to the act that possessed her. In the curious accent of Indians educated in England she spoke words she had written for him and for this occasion:

> Destroyer of scourges, generator of new life,
> Conqueror of craving, vessel of hope for the world,
> Avatar of truth for this yuga, *I salute thee!...*

Then, in her sari of soft pale blue, she prostrated before him on the gold-carpeted floor and held the posture a full minute while the silence high above the midtown streets assumed an identity of its own. And still he said nothing, nor did anything, filled with the significance of this moment of truth.

When it passed, with eyes downcast and hands still in the prayer position, she slowly rose to her feet and in the same deliberate, ritual-like motions shifted to the other armchair and at length, in a new silence flowing out of the first, began to speak, in her clipped, educated accent:

"That is why I have come, Bill, all the way from Madras, to perform those actions and to utter those words. You have been on my mind for more than two and a half years, ever since I happened upon a stray copy of the *Liberty* magazine article about you and AA, after which I wrote to the central office and heard about the Big Book, which I promptly ordered, received in due course, and read and reread many times with unabating wonder and conviction about its greatness, like the greatness of its author! From the very beginning I—a young but full-fledged alcoholic in my corner of the world—felt that the book spoke directly to me as nothing and no one ever had before, I felt I was with someone of my own kind for the first time, and what a relief it was! To discover that there were others far away suffering in the same mysterious and apparently incurable way that I had been, but who had found a solution and a way out thanks to the genius, wisdom and farsightedness of one man thrilled me as hardly anything else has ever been able to do! From the beginning I regarded the Big Book as a new kind of scripture and you, the author of its most important pages, as a prophet for our time in the great tradition of all the world's prophets, which as you may or may not know means so much to us in India. There we have a widespread belief that whenever there appears any authentic greatness in the world the Lord—the divine power—is manifesting through that. Which is what I felt in a powerful mystical way even when I studied the old *Liberty* piece. I said to myself, as I read between the lines, that here is something! Here is the beginning of a truly genuine new religion, and this man Bill W. is its prophet, perhaps the prophet the whole age has been waiting for!

"As for my own initiation into alcoholism, it is fairly ordinary. I was twenty at the time, in love with a young man I knew in our Madras district, and he, I believe, was in love with me. But ours was still a caste system, as you must know, and marriages were arranged. Each of us within a year was married off to other individuals, and despite the habit of my Hindu upbringing, I thought my heart would break. Until I discovered wine—which gave me easement for a long time. I had actually come to it when it was clear my true love and I would see little or nothing of each other after our marriages. From wine I moved on to stronger potions. Gradually I became known for what I was doing and disgraced my husband, who was a civil servant with the Madras State government, and my mother, who lived with us.

"The painful irony was that after a time I realized the young man I loved was now happily married—it had been a very good match for him and his wife, and when I contemplated the truth of things I was happily married too. My husband was a very good man and slowly I learned to love him and realized I had been dealt with very fairly by the gods. In reality, as between the two marriages, everything turned out well and I tried to be as accepting of what had happened as I could. But still I went on drinking! The genie was out of the bottle and could not be put back in! I had discovered the alcoholic *nature*. Purged of alcohol, seen in its essence, that nature was *me*. I have analyzed it into two dominant aspects. Firstly, alcoholism it seems to me, is an affliction of *loss,* of being bereaved of something infinitely precious which we never find again—or, it may be, some terrible, fixed disillusion with life which *nothing* can atone for. By your silence you seem to agree, Bill! It has been your portion also, that I know. The alcoholic is wounded by some irreparable loss, alcohol itself being merely his means of attempting to forget it, or to find it again in the sometimes roseate world of his intoxication!

"On the other hand, the alcoholic nature, *free of alcohol,* was a perfect and ideal me, an infinite and God-seeking nature! As you, dear Bill, from the Big Book alone, know all too well—know more profoundly than anyone! It is a subject I would fervently hope you will expand on at length some day—perhaps in your next book. It badly needs to be explored, as only you could do for us. Possibly also I in my small way may be able to impart to you something of the mysticism of India to shore up your own insights.

"And these two fundamental aspects of alcoholism—the psychological and the transcendental—are mutually related, integrally connected. The unhealed wound *can,* I believe, be healed—not of course by drinking nor by any other medicine this world affords—but by the spiritual, the *divine* element in our nature, that *is,* I believe, our nature ... awakening, coming into its own, and that would be done, would it not, by our conscious identifying with that element until it and our personality are one, and the deep wound that sent us to drinking for a cure is cured once and for all! Oh, Bill, if you could shed more light on *this* for us, comparable to what you have already done about drinking and the path to sobriety—that would be your crowning glory beyond any doubt!

"You have thought about all this many times yourself, I can see from your expression. I am telling you nothing new, I well realize that—please forgive me, my dear friend and guiding light, if I have seemed presumptuous. I do not mean to be, I assure you.

"Meanwhile—to return to my narrative—I was caught by the obsession of alcoholism, happy marriage or not, and went on compulsively drinking. I thought of suicide but for a Hindu that is simply *taboo,* an act of supreme *ignorance.* We believe the individual soul as an absolute existence is eternally real—permanently alive! *You can't escape!* Until we have the freedom of saints everything is karma, binding us one way or another, and such an action would only reap for me more bad karma in the next lifetime, would plunge me into a state even *worse!* ... You yourself believe in reincarnation. I see you nodding. It does not surprise me—you, being what you are, would have to believe in it. The author of the Big Book could not have had a mind limited by the one-life concept ... I had to live, then, there was no other option. So I went on drinking—daily, furtive, desperate drinking, not really alive, not really dead ... along with how many millions of others in just that condition around the world.

"And here I am speaking to the liberator of all of them—a true messiah and savior, if you will allow me to speak with such emotion on such short notice! Now do you understand why I've come here, why we are together, why I had to prostrate before you and say those things I did? You have told me coming here from India was a rare and impressive thing but that is really nothing. Doing so even a thousand times would not begin to match what you have done and what you now mean to the world...."

Her passionate words, the earnest, unequivocal tone of her cultured voice, her penetrating yet somehow deferent, self-abnegating glance, the eloquent, majestic posture of her body in the chair, all evoked for him a sense of depth, *spiritual* depth, quite unknown in the West. Unknown to *his* experience at least. Another world of consciousness was here with him in this anonymous room made memorable by their meeting, which he could not believe was accidental.

Somehow the cacophony of Times Square in the afternoon—although fully audible a few stories below through the half-opened window—did not disturb their communion, hardly seemed to reach their ears. The reality of some higher truth manifesting there between them was too strong to be disturbed by any combination of sense impressions from the world without.

She was describing her first year in Madras after reading the *Liberty* article and her discovery of the Big Book.

"There were two other women I knew who had trouble with alcohol, and both, like me, were secret, daily drinkers, deteriorating steadily. I brought them the magazine and the Big Book and they both read it—not with my enthusiasm but enough to join me in forming our own AA group—the first, I am sure, in Madras, and perhaps in all of India! Just the three of us. We would meet as though having a purely social friendly relationship, but we would confess our stories and experiences, our fears and longings, our hopes for a better life. We played a game, I should tell you, called "Bill and Dr. Bob"—we traced your career from Towns hospital to the Akron hotel and thence to the meeting with Dr. Bob!

"Unfortunately neither of them could stay sober for too long a period of time. But, even so, they were benefited, I know that, and when I return I shall spend hours trying to impart to them, and to any others like them I can find, the essence of what I've learned during these months.

"You may wonder about how I was able to get my trip to the West agreed to by my husband—and also by my mother, who, with him, had the means—which I did not—to finance the trip. In fact, it was not all that difficult, once they had seen that AA's program even from a remote distance was working, keeping me sober for month after month, when nothing for *years* had worked, including daily prayers to all the Hindu pantheon of gods to intercede, which did not happen of course because—as you have made so clear in the Book— the alcoholic has to *want* it—the grace, the power, the support—before it will come to him. As all of us have known from your dramatic recounting of your days at Towns hospital ... which I want to visit, Bill, if you will show me how to get there—and also 182 Clinton Street—these historic places that are really *shrines* for anyone who has been freed from alcoholism. And I only *wanted* it—truly wanted to stop—after reading *Liberty* and the Big Book, which I impressed upon my husband and mother, and they accepted my viewpoint, although my mother wanted to know why, since I had the AA teachings, I still had to go all the way to America to meet the founder. I told her that reading his thought was not enough. True, I had the teachings, but I had to feel the vital, life-enhancing *mana,* I had to see and hear and touch the *avatar!* And she accepted, as did my husband. After all, these are ancient Hindu assumptions and they were familiar with the psychology behind them. So they did not object too much, particularly once they realized I had my heart set on going. Between them they consented and enabled me to go. They shared the expense, including funds for the three months here, and they gave me their blessings. I told them I would not waste a minute. I assured them that I would steep myself in enough AA meetings and lore to last me a lifetime and teach me how to guide my three-member group back in Madras.... And that is what I have started to do and will continue...."

He knew she was in attendance at meetings every night all over Manhattan, including two on Sunday. She could not get enough, taking notes at each, asking the speakers questions afterwards, taking down phone numbers, ascertaining precise directions to the next meeting, her very being like a sponge of eager, insatiable receptivity to all she heard and discovered.

And everywhere she went she carried with her the Big Book, which she treasured and read constantly. It was a scripture for alcoholics, she told him—a historic, immortal work.

She had gotten up again and prostrated once more at full length on the floor, lying very still for perhaps a minute. After rising to her knees, her palms folded on her breast, she spoke again.

"I would like to end my prayer with an old Hindu chant that has always moved me. It seems very appropriate here and now:

> May the wicked become virtuous,
> May the virtuous obtain tranquillity,
> May the tranquil become free from bonds,
> May the freed make others free....

As she stood up, smiling, eyes downcast, she concluded: "The chant is for you, Bill! The significance is for you!..."

After he had left, the contrasting reality of Times Square was like plunging into a sea of turbulent life after a respite of contemplation on a desert island. Despite the otherworldly effect of her words, and the beguilement of her personality, as he walked to Forty-second Street, three blocks away, he did not fail, as though by instinct, to note the drunkards, potential and actual, who crossed his path, reminding him of the countless times he had blindly careened among these same fabled streets during his addictive years.

Feeling uplifted from their meeting, he had decided to walk back to his office in AA headquarters across town, instead of taking the bus. As usual, he had left his car with Lois in Bedford Hills during the day, for she would have more use for it.

Swinging east along Forty-second Street, he paused for the traffic light at Fifth Avenue, where the New York Public Library stood in all its splendor, guarded by its two stone lions.

He thought of Princess' confession and he realized that the very last thing she had said had puzzled him—her remarks about the freed making others free, the implication being that he himself was such a person.

How wrong she was.

He would have to talk to her about it at their next meeting. When that might be, he had no idea. It couldn't be every week, as she wanted.

There were so many eager to meet with him, even for a few minutes, so many letters to answer, some requiring precise and rigorous attention, so many requests to speak at meetings, so many conferences.

Free?

The irony struck him hard, though of course she had not meant freedom in precisely that way.

However she had meant it, he had to speak to her about it, for a misunderstanding in an area so basic would influence their future contacts. Which, he had to acknowledge, meant as much to him as apparently it did to her.

There was no mystery why he should want to maintain close relations during her all-too-brief months in the city: he was captivated with her—not as a romantic possibility but as representative of a kind of woman of which he had had practically no experience, whom he wanted to meet with to give himself not only the pleasure but the spiritual inspiration of her presence. From their single meeting he felt new vistas in the male-female relation had been opened to him.

As he walked through the thronging Grand Central district close to headquarters he realized that his enchantment lent her statements a persuasion and force he had found hard to resist.

Ostensibly she was in New York to learn, but actually, he believed, she was here to *speak*—to him. Speak words, utter wisdom—more than she knew—of which he stood in acute need. Truths no one else could frame, insights no one else could shape—for him to assimilate at a time when he needed most of all to hear her.

Filled with these mystic ruminations in the center of the modern world's secular city, he had reached the lobby of the midtown building that housed the AA main office and immediately his mood shifted to one of business-like seriousness and concentration. When he got off the elevator and approached the office he seemed to be trying to make himself invisible as he opened the door and *slouched* in. Upon his arrival, as always happened, everything stopped for a single isolated moment. Nell and the part-time secretaries looked up, paused, passed through a brief moment of adjustment, then returned to work. The half dozen people waiting patiently in the outer office, realizing who he was, the man they were there for, gazed up at him as he loped past in his long-legged stride, with peculiar, fixed, half-believing expressions. *Was this him?* they were asking themselves.

It was always this way, he reflected, as he took his jacket off and prepared to meet the first of his visitors.

Free? Again the question challenged him. Princess, you are mistaken.

Hence, *was* he, *could* he be, a prophet? In her presence she seemed to be able to persuade him of anything.

But was he?

They met again two weeks later in her hotel room, where once more she performed her ritual of prostration and devotion. Before he could bring up his questions he first had to answer a number of her own arising from her intense exposure to AA's program as well as from the ongoing state of her sobriety, which, he guessed, was in good condition.

"Is there any special word of wisdom you have for me, Bill, about making it easier to stay sober—beyond, of course—" she smiled, brown face and brown eyes radiant with feminine aura "—staying away from the first drink?"

"Don't get too tired, don't get too hungry, don't get too lonely—danger states, all, for a recovering alcoholic."

She went to the notebook she took to AA meetings and copied the words down immediately.

"And remember," he added, "the mind cannot entertain two ideas at the same time. If you are praying you cannot simultaneously be wanting to drink."

She opened her notebook again and recorded this idea as well.

"If I could see you enough, Bill, I wouldn't have to go to meetings!"

He demurred. Individual exchanges with one's sponsor—as he was to her—were vital, to be sure. "But attendance at meetings is even more so. It is at meetings—by our willingness *to* attend, a humble acceptance of our limitations against the threat of alcohol—where we express our dependence on the higher power manifested as the group. The ego has little room for leverage at such times."

This idea too, in its essence, went into the notebook.

He asked about her sobriety and whether she still felt the urge to drink.

"In fact," she said, "being here, at the very center of AA, and having contact with you personally, Bill, has wiped out, or *as if* wiped out, my desire to drink. To speak truthfully, from the day I determined to come to New York to this moment I have been free from the desire. It is as though I never had trouble of that kind and indeed never took a drink in my life!"

He warned her gently against overconfidence.

"'We are dealing with alcohol,'" she said, smiling, quoting a phrase from the Big Book, "'cunning, baffling, powerful!'..."

He remembered the hour and place when the passage had been penned.

Reminded of his modification of those words in the four years since then, he briefly debated whether introducing the fact just now would be wise, but decided to do so in view of the subtlety of her intellect and his strong intuition of the solid sobriety she had.

"Not only alcohol," he said tentatively, then added more firmly: "It is *mind* that is cunning, baffling, and powerful—the mind of the sober alcoholic when contemplating either the thought of a drink or the thought of a train of events that will lead to it. It is mind even more than alcohol we must overcome!"

Her face beamed, her eyes shone with admiration and something like gratitude.

"Of course you are right, Bill. It thrills me to hear you speak that way because it is just the kind of thing one of our Indian sages would have said! They believe—representing the ancient mystical tradition of India—that the mind is everything, source of all our misery and our happiness. They would say, speaking about alcoholics, for example, that when we are sober—in the AA way, that is—the mind is pacified, quiet, happy. It is because the mind, convinced that we are doing the right thing, is happy that *we* are. Thus, it is not even because of sobriety that we are happy but because of the state of our minds!

"In the same way we are miserable and frustrated when we drink— or when we *drank,* I should say—because the mind over time had learned that drinking was the one thing we must not under any circumstances do. Hence when we *do* it, the mind—acting now as our *conscience*—recoils in reaction, will not give us any peace, turns on us like an avenger, crucifies us with its burden of shame and guilt, and hounds us day and night until we are driven to surrender and give up the alcohol. So, again, it is the unappeased and angry mind that makes us unhappy when we drink more than the drinking *per se*. Do you see?

"Therefore the sages study the mind day and night—for it is a world in itself, the *whole* world, some of them say—those who are followers of Patanjali's yoga system, about which you must have heard *something,* I have no doubt. That is chiefly why they meditate so much— to study and master the mind and thus to bring themselves to the realization of Truth."

There was a significant pause as he pondered the implications of what she had said. "For them, as I follow you, the higher power would be the mind and not God as we understand him?"

She shook her head with a peculiar expression of delight on her face. "Truth, Bill—*Truth* would be. Mind is only the incomparable organ that brings us to that. For at the center of mind there is, they say—and all our holy books, the Vedas, the Gita, and all, confirm it—a reality that is not mind, that transcends mind, that is pure spirit, pure *Brahman,* our Sanskrit name for the godhead, the divine ground of being, also known as *Truth*—" She smiled. "So I have *heard*. Mind, Bill, is the way to all that, the field, the territory we must traverse before reaching the goal. On *this* side of the divine world, mind is supreme. But once the mind is understood, mastered, and purified, the mystic transcends mind and goes to the goal directly."

Her grasp of these otherworldly subtleties dazzled him. He could not but wonder about her possible actual experience of them.

She seemed to read his thought. "I speak from hearsay," she said, smiling again, drawing her chair closer to his in her pleasure at the turn the conversation had taken. "Not from experience. It is the same with all of us in India. We have heard these wonderful ideas, and seen the great mystics, or at least *know* of them, and instinctively we appropriate their transcendental teachings to ourselves and act—as I have done just now—as though we know from first-hand knowledge what we are talking about! We hear the sages discussing constantly about meditation, glorifying it as the way to the highest spiritual realization, and we do the same there too. As I have!"

She stopped, looked searchingly at him, and abruptly asked: "Do *you* meditate, Bill? As a serious thing?"

He was a little shocked at her candor but carefully hid his feelings, gave no indication of how he had reacted. Quietly—aware of his dissembling—he told her that he meditated often, in various places, sometimes with Lois in the morning, frequently while driving or riding home late in the train from Grand Central.

She smiled tolerantly at what he had said.

"I mean *really* meditate? As a discipline! You are a modern prophet, Bill—and all prophets must learn to meditate, it is the great thing that distinguishes them from others. I don't know how myself. If I know so much about meditation and spiritual matters why did I become an alcoholic! You must have asked yourself that question—" He smiled awkwardly. He had been weighing the very thought. "—It is the same with meditation as with the sublime yoga and mystical philosophies of India, we Hindus act as if we know all about meditation when in fact we know little if anything about it. Except for the mystics, we just prattle about it, like children imitating adults. To speak frankly, Bill, I myself do not know how to meditate. For one very good reason— you have to be *called* to meditate, to be able to do it at all ... as you, Bill, if I may say so, have been called. Thus yours is a completely different case from most people. If you don't know how to meditate, Bill, then learn! It is up to you to find out. Because if you don't learn, you will perhaps deprive your life of what it is most now in need of, as the next stage in your evolution looms...."

Involuntarily he was thinking of Chris Eastman and his similar message.

He gave her the impression of listening wisely, as though agreeing with everything, but keeping his own counsel. How could he inform her of what his views really were? At the same time his restraint created a spirit of discretion: argumentation in so delicate an area might disillusion her hero-worship.

"... I do believe most earnestly that meditation is more than you have indicated in the Big Book—step eleven, for example. I wouldn't think of suggesting you even dream of changing it. But meditation is really—to speak in all candor, my dear friend—*more* than what you and those following in your footsteps have declared."

He felt an impulse to object but continued to exercise prudence, not only because of awareness of his spiritual delinquency since the moment at Towns eight years before but because he knew he was in the presence of someone who, for all her disclaimers about being a mere prattler of things mystical, knew far more about them than he was ever likely to. He suspected it was ethnic—that Hindus and Buddhists had more powerful intuitions into religious truth than almost any Westerner or Christian he could name.

He was suddenly alerted at her casual introduction of the theme of freedom.

"Freedom, spiritual freedom, *is*—as they see it in India—the purpose of life. And it is meditation that indispensably leads to it. Without a lifelong consecration to the practice of daily, and more than daily, meditation, they tell us over and over, there is no possibility of gaining freedom from the karma—that is to say, the burden of personality weaknesses—that envelops us. Saintliness is merely another word for that goal of freedom. The saint is the man who has won freedom, has rescued himself from the waters of worldliness and self-love! And, in certain cases, from alcoholism too! Meditation leads us, or may lead us—if we are pursuing an ethical and spiritual life—to saintliness, to freedom, and thence to winning the power to make *others* free. You will remember that line from the ancient chant I recited last time—" He nodded, warily silent. "—As I said then, Bill, I had you in mind when I came to those lines—" he made a gesture of protest "—but it's true, you *have* made others free!"

He reminded her that he was far from being a free man by any standard.

"Free to do what you want—no. I realize that. In AA you are the man in everybody's sight and can hardly make a move but it is studied. I have come to understand that quite well, even during the short time I have been in New York. Your condition is like that of a saint. He also is the man in everyone's view, the man constantly watched and evaluated to discover if he *is*, really and truly, a saint. I see you protest at my suggesting such a comparison, but it is true—after all, you have had the spiritual experience, that time in Towns, which has put us all in its debt, and in *your* debt, for yours was the experience of truth—"

"A very limited—"

"Limited it *may* have been, but it was *genuine,* it was from the Supreme, and even a fraction of what the full experience might have been—those that actual saints and mystics experience—was enough to set you apart from others. And the harvest it has reaped—not only your own sobriety, Bill, but that of growing thousands of others! The vast new world of AA itself is its harvest!

"So neither you nor the saint is free in the sense of being able to *do* what you want. On the contrary, you and he are of all men the *least* able to do so, for the reasons we well know. The saint, too, is vulnerable to the slightest suspicion; he must not only be virtuous but *appear* to be so—he must not only always keep himself in the presence of the divine but must at the same time remain conscious of the weaknesses of men's minds, their ignorance of higher truth, their eternal proneness to thinking the worst of others.

"Therefore freedom to *do* was not what I meant in that ancient Vedic chant about freedom, for freedom to *do* is merely political or social or sexual freedom—*karmic* freedom, which is all that most can achieve and is the kind of freedom most people have in mind when they use the word at all.

"I was thinking of a freedom *beyond* karma, the freedom to *be,* in a word, the freedom *from* karma and its illusions, freedom *from* alcoholism—which you have achieved and through your continuing example and your wisdom have showed the way for the rest of us to go.

"To be free *from* desires rather than free to give *into* them—that is the freedom that *is* freedom, my good friend. *Spiritual* freedom, Bill. It is the soul's rather than the body's freedom. Freedom of the spirit, not freedom of the ego. Freedom to turn our mind and will toward the divine and gradually *resemble* the divine rather than the freedom to be *ourselves*—our lower, weaker, ego-ridden, karma-dominated selves. It is, finally, the freedom from the desire to have the other lower freedom, the freedom merely to *do*. Freedom from *that* freedom—that is freedom!"

She paused, beaming with happiness that she had been able to phrase such thoughts. He sat speechless with admiration. She had not only made clear the idea that had previously troubled him but had done it in her own way and at her own time. He smiled in gratitude.

"'May the freed make others free'," she said, her gaze level with his. There was nothing more to say.

In his journal he wrote:

... While communicating fundamental principles of the religion of India, she probes me personally and I believe means to do so at each meeting we may have. Without appearing to, she applies to my spirit pressures of a subtle and distinctive kind, leaving me both fascinated—and unable to exorcise a guilt whose potential she has abundantly tapped.

I cannot deny that my crowded schedule day after day in the coming weeks, both in New York and at group anniversaries elsewhere, forbidding much likelihood of frequent future meetings, does not displease me. Grateful as I am for her company and wisdom, and always impressed by her, I sometimes feel that she uses her genuine hero-worship, her feeling of something like reverence for me, as justification for her penetrating shafts of insight and admonition ... even though I know she is right in what she implies—inspired, and conscious herself of the truth of her words. Words few others have heard, with implications few others have confronted.

Ever since Towns these questions—of mysticism, of greater spiritual commitment to the path that leads to God-realization, even at the possible cost of what it might mean to the life of AA—have been with me. Only through my paramount dedication to AA itself have I been able, more or less successfully, to divert my mind from any too-zealous contemplation of them.

Until now. Until the Princess, with her message from the forests of India. And she is right—as far as she sees, without sufficiently evaluating my particular problems.

But I turn away....

It had been weeks since he had felt free enough to open his journal. Despite its pressures, the hectic pace of his organizational life ever since the meteoric effect of the Alexander article had left him generally comfortable with his own state of mind—relatively able, thus far, to handle intrusive trains of thought without much difficulty. But since meeting Shivani he had found himself resorting to the self-revelation of the journal with a sense of urgency he had not known since January of 1942.

Likewise, he arranged to meet her, in their remaining encounters, in public places, where the mood of secret communication intimated in her Times Square hotel room was missing, and where he could control their discussion more easily.

Since she was increasingly filled with the psychology of AA mediated through the steady succession of nightly meetings, it was natural to spend most of their time over coffee in restaurants near his office discussing the endless questions he urged her to pose to him, which left little opportunity for the earlier themes.

Should she attend primarily open or closed meetings—or both? Should she speak only at one or the other—or both? In view of her brief tenure in New York should she become anyone's sponsor? Should she avoid eating-places where liquor was served? Did milk chocolate really overcome, as she had heard, the desire to drink—and, if so, should she carry a bar in her purse? Should she search for *reasons* why she became an alcoholic?

Before commenting on the last he took time to collect his thoughts and then addressed her in a vein more serious than usual:

"Wander into that psychological maze and you will never get out—and may drink again. The *reasons* for our drinking are manifold but to take that merely rational approach to its solution is to invite failure and often disaster. Those who do so—psychiatrists, for example—have had negligible success with patients, for they are dealing with a soul-malady not subject to the usual weapons of psychotherapy. Only a multi-leveled attack on the problem, such as we take in AA, offers much success. Ultimately only a spiritual program has proved to be the answer ... though there are some nonspiritual programs that have been helpful to those who refuse to think of the higher power.

"Eventually, Princess, after a few years of good sobriety, we do discover the *reasons,* it becomes apparent and *obvious* why we became alcoholics, we *know*—as we can never know in the early months— why we drank the way we did, what we were looking for—"

"God-consciousness, Bill?"

She was looking at him with her dark, Oriental, all-knowing gaze, fixing him with her glance.

He nodded, letting his silence speak.

On the way back to his office he brooded over her last remark, as he had over previous ones weeks before. She always seemed to be speaking to a part of him of which no one else, even Lois, was aware.

Of which he himself was not. She seemed to awaken it to sudden life.

Was it true, then—God-consciousness? It had felt true when she said it, and when he had concurred. And if it was, well, here he was in a position—and had been for eight years past—to do something about it, to bring to realization that for which he had burned up his life year after year.

Was sobriety enough, after all?

An alternative to God-consciousness?

In retrospect he could not clearly recall the time and manner of her leave-taking. She seemed to slip away, gradually seeing him less and less, not only because of his desire but her own: she would not press him unduly. She seemed to feel his withdrawing reticence after the unique rapport and mutual revelations of the early meetings and accepted what she sensed.

He opened his studio desk drawer and found the letter she wrote to him soon after her return to Madras. *"My dear Bill,"* she had begun and then had described the progress of the infant AA movement in Madras, of which she was clearly the acknowledged leader. "—We are running the meetings just like AA in New York with the slight difference that at the end we do not recite the Lord's Prayer but instead adapt to local religious customs, which you always recommended people do anyway.

"I am in great demand here, as Bill W.'s Asian deputy! I have become famous as the woman who all alone went halfway around the globe to meet the world's premier master of alcoholism. My copy of the Big Book is being read by several people at the same time, and everything I remember you telling me has been communicated to them and they have memorized it, as though it was the teaching of a great Indian sage—and I, for one, as well you know, literally think of you in those terms. Last night I gave a special talk on you and your works—'The Meaning of Towns and Akron'—and concluded my presentation with a sentence that brought a round of applause. I told them that you had conquered the desire to drink in a spirit of surrender and conveyed the message in a spirit of service—the first ever to do so!"

He found himself warming at the praise.

Then her letter grew more somber, evasive, and her real purpose in writing became clear. "... I didn't mention it to you in New York but I have—or believe I have—the gift of seeing into the future. Just as millions of others do in India or think they do. It is our substitute for embracing the path, the real path of the mystics and sages. At any rate I seem to have that gift, or tendency, and what it reveals—for what it may be worth—is sorrow ahead for you. Not grief from bereavement, for example, for the condition of sorrow seems very protracted. And not drinking, of course, but rather a darkness continuing year after year, for many years, to commence fairly soon, I am sorry to have to tell you—perhaps in less than a year ... some kind of mysterious gloom or heaviness or depression, as though you are carrying—and will continue to do so—a great secret burden known only to yourself. And to speak truthfully, my vision—or clairvoyance, or whatever we might call it—does not show it ending. I am terribly upset to have to tell you all this, Bill, but I think I would have felt worse had I said nothing at all...."

She did not say what the burden was, or even what she thought it was. But she knew. They both did. It was what she had come to New York for—to show him the burden, its sorrow, and its mystery, without naming it, leaving it up to him to discover.

She died some nine months later in an automobile accident in a Madras street. The driver of the death-car was found to be under the influence of alcohol.

Her husband sent him the news, adding poignantly that "Shivani's last two years, including the year after her New York trip and the year prior to it were full of happiness for her and for all who knew her. For which you personally must take the credit. We are grateful here for all you have done—no words can express our gratitude. I am sure that among her last thoughts you would have found an honored place. Both her mother and myself have always felt there was something divinely prophetic about her trip to New York to meet you, though what the deeper implications might be, I am sure that was passed between the two of you and no others...."

He sat for some minutes in the soft but powerful grip of memory.

Yes. Prophetic. With implications they never had to speak about.

18   The Trauma

Had the Princess been with him at the brink of the Grand Canyon a year after she left, she might have helped him bring to consciousness the source and meaning of the nameless terror. But she was not. He was thrown on his own resources, unaided by a Lois captured by a creature's pride in robust normalcy that mocked his show of feebleness.

What led up to it, and to what lay beyond, reflected, like the moment itself, the same sense of inevitability.

The background was the unremitting schedule month after month that constituted his lifestyle, and had been such for several years now. It had given him the excuse to maintain sufficient distance from Shivani and the discomfort of her insights but he had not exaggerated the pressure it had exerted not only on his time but on his nerves and even more so in the year since her departure.

Almost every night in the week—overwhelmed by the endless correspondence and the large number of drop-in visitors—he worked late, was often the last to leave the office, turn out the lights, and either catch the final Westchester-bound commuter train for Bedford Hills or stay in a hotel. In addition there were the constant claims on his time to speak at anniversaries or to lend his presence at one or another of the new groups springing up everywhere. Because the East contained far more of these than the rest of the country, except for Ohio, and because yielding to their requests would take up less of his limited time, he had thus far not often ventured into the Midwest beyond Ohio, where, because of his frequent conferences with Dr. Bob, he was almost as familiar a figure as in New York.

But by the fall of 1943 demands from more distant places made it difficult not to accommodate them, particularly after they had in every case raised money to defray his traveling expenses. Plans were made, including a detailed itinerary of ten Western states, beginning in late October, the whole trip—the longest he had taken since AA's inception—to extend over three full months. Lois was to go with him. The climax was to be a visit to California where groups were rapidly mushrooming throughout the golden state.

Even after all the arrangements had been made and confirmations received from numerous cities, he found himself resisting.

"You have put this off much too long, Bill," Lois reminded him. "You know how they want you."

That might be the problem. Their *wanting* him, their potential for devouring him ... even as they offered him, in compensation—*themselves*. Yet, apart from the physical locales, what did he have to fear that was really unfamiliar? He had spoken at enough AA meetings in the last few years to have a good idea of what the experience was basically going to be like.

Perhaps among unfamiliar faces, where both he and his audiences would be seeing each other for the first time, it would be like starting the whole phenomenon all over again, renewing the powerful experience that seized him with every group he addressed, every audience that opened itself to him—heart and soul—so uniquely ... each time giving rise to the same series of emotions and self-searchings he had known from the beginning.

So it would be that all over again, except—because of its complete newness—more intensely, more nakedly than before. Thus, although confident of what he could do, he was pessimistic about what the experience, repeated so many times over a limited period, would do to *him*.

What he needed was a perspective that would enable him to approach the problem in a new light, from opposite points of view: theirs and his. But he had no idea what that might be.

They and he. Like two entities. Two halves of a single reality, a common life. Each dependent on the other, each controlling the other.

Each given an existence, an identity, through the other.

At Chicago, Omaha, and Denver he encountered fervent receptions, with, he knew, a foretaste of greater ones to come. He was greeted in each city like a conquering hero, awaking in him moods of dismay mingled with irrepressible pride. In each case hundreds came out to hear him—to *see* him, rather. Lois, too, realized he was facing a more impassioned response than he had had in the East, where he had been a known presence, involved in controversy like anyone else, an only partly legendary figure. But here he was all legend, a historic name stepped out of an epic background and immediately there before them.

Something had opened up in him, not to be denied. It was as though the cheers were coming from some depth within himself.

A strange nervous excitement filled him, bringing a fear he had not known.

At the Grand Canyon, en route to Los Angeles, the depth became palpable and real, threatening to draw him into its maw, with Lois— confident, untroubled—standing beside him in his sudden terror. Never before had he experienced this kind of phobia, never before had the potential for submersion and obliteration so awakened.

A feeling of instant peril seized him. The abyss below, the abyss within. The sight of the depths to which he could sink plunged him into a state of dread, unbearable vertigo.

In California the adulation intensified—as he had known it would: the Canyon terror being a herald of things to come, as well as a reflection of what had already taken place. The fervor was now *different* ... like what St. Paul would have received on his travels. They greeted him as a messiah, not as a man. They wanted to *touch* him and thus make secure their own lives, magically protect them from untoward influences.

He complained to Lois: "They never tire of hearing the same story—familiar to all of AA by now—over and over!"

"It is not a story any more, Bill, it's a legend—the basic AA history!"

He realized again the prophetic, epic nature of his life. He had had a dream and, behold, it had come to pass. He had uncovered an infinite vein of human nature, like a prophet of old; had emerged from some secret gulf of experience and was now facing others like someone returned from the dead.

In the California halls, where the mass meetings brought out a thousand to hear him speak each time, it was like another Canyon opening to devour him. His audience stood roaring their approval and love, like souls rescued from the horrors of hell by the man standing before them, the mythic figure from the East. They would not let him start, would not let him finish, would not stop applauding.

It was like an encounter with God, this penetration into such naked humanity. It was what he had always wanted, but having brought it to pass, found it too much—this sea of upturned faces rapt with acclaim, this avalanche of cheers.

The AA he had discovered in 1941, following the impact of the Alexander article, had been only a promise and a potential. *This* was AA itself, the living reality, and far more potent in its effect on his psyche was the *personal* factor ... momentous because of the power it asserted over him, and over his life, which no longer belonged to him. *Others* had mastered him, *others* were now living through him.

When he finally did speak, an uncanny silence fell upon the audience. He spoke without notes, without plan or organization, plunging into his own story, told and retold so many times in the East— precisely what they insisted on hearing from him. Two hours of extempore oratory somehow passed. No one left the hall. A mysterious presence had closed in upon speaker and audience, dictating what he would and could say. Somehow he gave them what they wanted, although almost immediately afterwards he could not remember what it was that he had said.

In the midst of the furor he could not but notice his mother's ambivalent struggle to be pleased and proud as she sat next to Lois at the front of the hall. Widowed a few years earlier, after a second marriage to a physician, she was now resident in San Diego and had come up to Los Angeles for the great occasion. When each of the thousand in the audience rose as her son walked out on the platform she turned to Lois with a look of shocked amazement. Later, Lois said, she spoke of "all the fuss" made over him. "—Everyone getting to their feet *on cue* when he walked to the lectern, as though he was a saint! And all the applause, and wanting to *touch* him or grab his hand afterwards, as though he was another *Christ*!"

"That is almost how they think of him," Lois said quietly.

"But *pride*," his mother warned. "There is the danger of *pride*. The *sin* of pride!"

Thus casting her emotional conflicts in the light of concern for his moral well-being.

As he gazed intermittently in her direction, the stresses she was going through at the sight of him receiving such homage were visibly registered on her face. Which did not surprise him: her lifelong conviction of his immaturity and selfishness was not likely to be erased by any evidence, however dramatic, to the contrary. What did surprise him was that he felt no dismay or even disappointment that even now, even here, she should still be feeling as she did.

It flashed swiftly through his mind that it was as if she had gained more satisfaction in 1934 in being asked by Dorothy to help pay for his hospitalization at Towns than by the sight of that same son a decade later being idolized to a greater degree than hardly anyone had ever been in America. What astonished him was that the thought induced no bitterness. He saw it consumed in the storm of emotion raging through his blood, and through the blood of one thousand others.

With the preternatural power of intuition which the moment gave him, he knew that the quasi-mystical exaltation he was undergoing with the audience was far more vital than the childhood-misery nuances which the sight of his mother in her torment of self-doubt had passingly reawakened.

His relation to the AA disciples—for as such he saw them—was truly like an experience of God manifesting through the audiences, the rapt and self-abandoned acolytes at the altar of his own history and his presence there before them ... caught up, despite anything he might wish to do about it, in a self-transcending ecstasy that matched their uplifted state: giving him such tribute ... giving him everything they were capable of.

Giving him their lives.

By comparison the old guilts and unworthiness stemming from so long ago, fleetingly outpictured on his mother's strained countenance, were less substantial things.

What he was going through in the meetings was reality. It was truth.

But a reality from which he wished to flee, and from which he *would* flee. He had made his decision: flight, escape, withdrawal. A passion for seclusion, for self-contemplation, possessed him.

Already, as he stood on the platform, he was *willing* the commencement of the life that was his for nearly six fruitless years, with as many more looming.

Coming just then, the chance to spend a few days of rest at a monastery retreat in Trabuco Canyon an hour's drive south of Los Angeles was like balm for his soul—and for the tired Lois too. A Hollywood AA member, one Dave D., had made the offer to bring him into contact with the resident philosopher-mystic at the monastery, the English author and Orientalist, Gerald Heard.

This learned and articulate man, spiritually ambitious for himself and for the mystical philosophies he had espoused, together with fellow British expatriates Christopher Isherwood and Aldous Huxley, constituted an early avant garde of Vedantic commitment in America. To attract the founder of the sensational Alcoholics Anonymous movement into their fold would provide the crusade with a special panache that was prominently in their mind when Bill and his wife were invited to recuperate for three or four days from their intensive labors.

"The man for the age!" Heard saluted him. He was a bearded ascetic in the British style.

By the third day they began their proselytizing, more comprehensively and with a bolder intention than what he remembered from Shivani's similar efforts. But the timing was poor. Depleted by the effort to adjust to the reality of his role in AA as it had now become so clear, he was in no condition to start adjusting to Heard's conception of him as a laymen's prophet—a new type of religious figure for a new age, with AA his band of sinners ready to mount towards higher levels of consciousness if he but gave the word and showed the way.

Even when the slender, tweed-wearing Huxley arrived, he felt no rush of enthusiasm. "To your other talents we must now add, from all reports, an orator's eloquence" were Huxley's words of greeting, and from the way he proffered his thin scholar's hand it was apparent, despite the intellectual renown of the one and the general obscurity of the other, which of the two was being flattered by the introduction.

Such was the stir his speeches had created in Southern California. And yet even now, in the tranquillity of the Trabuco retreat, looking back over the last several weeks with as much concentration as he could manage, he had only a vague remembrance of what he had actually said. Emotion, reaction, engulfing all-absorption in the moment, had been everything. Words, ideas, had mattered little. It was not *he* who had spoken, but some autonomous power within him, assuming authority as his ordinary, familiar self sank beneath the accolades that washed over him like ever-brimming waves. A mysterious *other,* a newer, profounder Self had spoken, had stilled the audiences, and now stood aloof from his conscious attempt at recall.

The Self that these Vedantists were invoking, perhaps. Shivani's *Atman.* And Chris Eastman's. The self of the mystics.

A version, too, of the consciousness that had possessed him that night in Towns nine years ago.

It was therefore highly ironic that Heard and Huxley should persistently keep alive for the last part of his stay at the monastery the option of mysticism when during their exchanges—his almost entirely a passive, listening role—and for some weeks before, his mind had been swimming in its own secret seas of mysticism.

Others besides Huxley offered him the boon of praise. "Mesmerizing," was one of the descriptions of his two-hour talks. And similar encomiums, which he accepted in the same nonreacting, inwardly baffled manner. The praise meant nothing. He had not earned it, had not understood the source of it. He felt more disoriented than ever. It was not only the new thousands, growing into tens of thousands, who perplexed and pressed him to the wall, but something indescribable within himself.

That, surely, had first to be addressed. To that end he appreciated the solitude they gave him, the extensive library, the open valley fields surrounding the retreat houses. They had even provided him and Lois with separate though adjacent bedrooms, by this gesture doubtless encouraging them to contribute to the prevailing monasticism of their environs.

Yes, that had to be first comprehended before he did anything else. For *that* he would need a great deal of solitude, not only here but in Bedford Hills. He looked ahead to the prospect with a voracious hunger.

On the fourth and last day at the retreat he thanked them for their hospitality but as for their suggestion that he consider the way of the mystic as the next and logical step in his career—in everything he did he had to keep in mind the best interests of AA.

He did not expect that these two men, each remarkable in his way, each distinguished among their fellows, could look at him, as he was departing, with envy.

• • •

After California there were still several states of the Southwest to be gotten through. In the grip of his trauma, he sleepwalked his way past the remaining weeks, moving in a half-trance of withdrawal and deep self-doubt even in the midst of the smiles and handshakes he habitually offered to one and all—to cast off suspicion that there was anything he might not want uncovered. Throughout these final days in Arizona, Texas, Oklahoma, and Arkansas his thoughts were constantly on the life he might cling to in his private refuge at Bedford Hills, a reassuring expectation as the last of the western journey was accounted for.

Under a leaden winter sky with a light thick snow falling—an omen, perhaps—they arrived at Manhattan's dark cavernous Pennsylvania Station on a Saturday late in January. Without delay they taxied the mile and a half across town to Grand Central. Although Lois was clearly in the mood for a welcoming committee, he was in no condition for celebrations and had insisted that they keep the exact time of their arrival secret.

That the main AA office would be closed except for volunteers manning the phones was a comfort as they sped northward from the city to their home. Lois held his hand in the train, her fingers pressing his with the enthusiasm she felt over the dramatic success of the trip.

"Not only Heard and Huxley but luminaries everywhere coming out to greet you, to share in the universal tribute. If you had any doubt before, dear Bill, now you can rest assured in what esteem you are held!"

When she asked why he had been so quiet for so long, contrary to what she would have expected, he told her he was talked out.

He craved the presence of his own solitude. That at least is how he thought of it: that what he was planning would have *spiritual* consequences and he himself was willing it. But he was already in the power of the adversary which, upon his arrival at their house, rose up from the underworld within and drew him down without delay.

So decisive, so instant, so total—it gave fateful promise of *lasting*.

When Monday came he asked Lois to call the office and tell them he was suffering from exhaustion and would need a full week at home

to recover. It was to be the first of many more such calls he would ask
her to make.

It was truly exhaustion: he could not move from his bed. Lois felt
panic at the prospect of whatever it was that had so mysteriously
attacked him. A man who should be sitting at the top of his world was
lying prostrate beneath it.

19   The Insight

Then without overture the cave-life began.
The days, often the weeks of inanition, the bone-deep lethargy,
the scalding self-contempt that led to no change, no vista that promised
any.

Years consumed by the lethal softness of the daily encroachment,
the deadly seduction of his will in the embrace of the dark presence—
no alien to his own identity, merely the other side of it.

Unable to break through despite, as he protested, and as Lois knew,
"trying everything."

Wrenching himself to manage two limited days a week at the
office, offering the excuse of low energy and time needed on *Twelve
Steps and Twelve Traditions,* which, he said, was "moving slowly." They
noted his lack of vitality, his sluggishness where before the brilliance
was one of his hallmarks. Accepting his transparent excuses, they tried
not to spread the word beyond their circle.

Where finally had his long exploration of the labyrinth of memory
brought him?

For one thing, the narrative had ended in California. Except for
the advent of Chris Eastman a few years ago, no arresting or dramatic
experiences nor the likelihood of any had happened to him since. For
the past five and a half years he had not so much been living as *reliving*—
vegetating, broodingly reminiscent over what once had been his life.

The other discovery, the chief one, was the acceptance of what had occurred in Los Angeles.

If there had been the slightest doubt what he meant to AA, *and what AA meant to him;* or if he had succeeded, prior to the western trip, in persuading himself that there *was* some doubt, he had to be left in no uncertainty whatever about his real status, his mythic role in the lives of tens of thousands.

The trauma of the California receptions had given him that knowledge overwhelmingly.

The experience had been the culmination not only of the long-postponed western trip but of his whole life. All roads had led to it, and the character of the years since then had been *determined* by it.

Against the backdrop of the acclaim, their need of him and the possession they had taken of him, the permanent binding of his destiny with AA had been forged in an instant and, in the years since, the realization had only intensified.

His long journey in remembrance, telescoping into a brief span of hours the course of half a century, had been worth the effort if it had reimpressed upon his brain the truth glimpsed so irrevocably in California. Resisted at the time—emotionally combated and turned from in something like panic. But gradually, then completely accepted, and now—thanks to the therapy of recollection—become part of his being as implicit in its truth as the air he breathed.

A somewhat surprising phenomenon was the persistence of the purely spiritual challenge. It was so much so that eventually the mystical alternative to the role cast for him by the epiphany in California became the strongest option to consider.

But, in view of his long-held secret sympathy with the idea, not really surprising. The coming of Chris Eastman during the depths of his depression was evidence enough. Chris, so identified with meditation and the mystical principle in religion, would not have assumed such importance for him in so short a time, particularly during such a dark period, had not his preoccupation with mysticism been fascinating to himself as well.

The lure of the mystic way had tempted him more than drinking could have done, more than Catholicism, for it had seemed the path to truth itself.

His close study of James' *Varieties,* a work saturated in the atmosphere of mysticism, his reading of the book over and over and freely commenting on it—perhaps a bit too freely—should have alerted others to his drawing to mysticism and its recondite ideal. But it had not. Only Chris had guessed.

Vividly he recalled now his grappling with the California enlightenment when it was still fresh, imagining every possible kind of scenario. To some extent he had discussed it with Chris, who intuited his deep, unrecognized affinities and, quietly encouraging him, had declared that anyone given the grace of experiencing such adulation, with a messiah-like influence over so many, had obviously been singled out by the divine as a man apart.

Had he been able, said Chris, to perceive the homage as a divine summons, he would have been able to attain spiritual conversion in terms of AA itself. "Instead you have avoided both acceptance *and* rejection in favor of a no-man's land of agonizing indecision."

In the tranquil womb of his studio he could understand all this much more clearly now, could see that the passionate hero-worship, the tireless willingness to hear him say the same things over and over, had come from the beyond. So rare an experience could not have had any other source. Once more it was being made plain to him that he had been chosen to become something like the founder of a new religion.

Chris' advice was sound. If he had answered the call directly he would not have had to leave AA or his position in it (as if he ever could!) and join a monastery or anything of that sort. Rather, as Shivani had urged him, he would learn at last to *truly* meditate, would consult with Chris for suggestions and for books to read, and write to Gerald Heard and Aldous Huxley for any ideas *they* could provide.

He persuaded himself to believe that in the course of things there was a good chance he could achieve a new spiritual destiny in a one-to-one relation to the deity even as he gave himself to AA ... *now* interpreting the acclaim as a divine action inducing him to connect with the fellowship in a different mode: strong, new-born, messianic, prophetic.

The divine had conceived of him in this light—could he not do the same?

Sainthood was perhaps a matter of self-expectation: saints were those who expected they would *become* saints.

"This is the will of God: namely, your *sanctification*." In a word, your saintliness. He heard again Chris' light-textured, gently urgent voice citing the passage from St. Paul.

No, he would not have to go anywhere but where he was. All the change required would be internal. Chris had stressed this.

The idea had excited him. Could he make it come to pass? Would it mean more than he could manage?

He brooded, wondered, waited. The weeks went by.

The insight faded. He lost his hold upon it. He seemed to forget just what it was that had thrilled him.

The inspiration converted into its opposite. Once disregarded, the potential that had lifted him up in excited anticipation became a power to sink him deeper into the darkness of himself that Shivani had visioned as "continuing."

In his journal he had copied out a passage from a letter Chris had sent him: "Those called to lead great enterprises of a spiritual nature do not receive their wisdom nor their experience with impunity. Their suffering is directly proportionate to the degree of their negligence."

In other words, truth, when resisted—and believed to *be* truth—became self-transformed into a new wave of depression.

Or *something* in him resisted, implacably, beyond his comprehension. Then slowly he understood.

There were degrees of truth, and kinds of truth. A man should obey the prompting of the highest truth he could apprehend. For *him*, his role in AA was that. The truth of mysticism was great and wondrous, he was certain of that. Had he been Chris, there would have been no doubt what path he would want to follow. But since he was himself, he had to follow his own highest truth—the relationship ordained for him with AA, now and for as long as he could presently see.

He had known this from the outset of Chris' seductive recommendation, had known where it would have to end. He had brooded endlessly over his offer, wrote probingly in his journal, and asked a series of ambiguous questions of his gifted young mentor.

He would still continue to do everything he was doing now? Yes, he would, said Chris. But wouldn't he begin to *look* different after, say, two or three years? He would. And *seem* different? Yes: the power of meditation would make itself felt throughout his personality. And speak and act different? Yes. Better, perhaps—but unquestionably different? Yes. He would be noticed? He would be. Attract attention? To some degree, yes. And the books he would be reading would be exotic, strange? Yes. How would it be if someone met him on the Westchester train reading *The Tibetan Book of the Dead* or *The Gospel of Sri Ramakrishna*—would it not cause rumors and anxieties ... talk? Yes.

The risk was too great. He could not do it. He could not forget where he had come from, what had nearly happened to him, could not forget the inferno that had been his life and would be the life again of any of tens of thousands of recovered alcoholics in AA who, disturbed by ambivalences and perplexities in his behavior, would use this knowledge as an excuse to return to the destructive path.

For *him* there must not only be no drinking but no Catholicism, no mysticism, and nothing whatever that would result in sentencing his fellows—groping, oversensitive souls as many of them were, beneath their aggressive and pathetic behavior—to a fate worse than death. Nothing at all.

Again the realization pressed home to him that that was why it had been made abundantly clear what he and AA meant to each other—and he had caught the message, had resisted it, run from it, but had never forgotten it, and now with the help of time and his exploration in the forests of the past he had more than ever accepted it.

Make no waves of any kind. *Keep everything as it has been.* Now especially, with Dr. Bob soon to die, as all predicted, it was more imperative than ever that the sole survivor of the Akron illumination preserve the established order of things with an unswerving devotion.

Whatever his life lacked, whatever *he* lacked, he was certain he would do *that*. Even a path he had seemed destined for—the shining mystic way of meditation and yoga—would not sidetrack him.

Perhaps in the *next* life he could undertake the rigors of mysticism and the pursuit of perfection. There would be time then.

But for now ... there was no time.

Month after month, and finally year after year, he went over the ground of his dilemma, his conflict surpassing anything he knew....

If he yielded to Chris, met the new challenge, and became a mystic, he would advance himself spiritually—and AA would suffer.

He felt like Moses given a glimpse of the promised land, then denied the experience of it. Through Chris, the California Vedantists and Shivani, as well as through his own private investigations, and the memory of Towns, it had been made clear to him what life's greatest prize could be.

And then forced to turn away from the vision.

The same power that had showed him the true way had showed him his dilemma—and blocked his escape.

It was more than a conflict or an impasse, it was a trap—one laid by divine providence. Hence what could psychology do to liberate him?

Introspection was more profitable. It could help him to *accept,* which, after today, he might better be able to do.

There was no doubt that Chris, the Princess and the California mystics had been right as far as their perception went, but he was right in opposing them. He knew as few did the quicksilver mentality of the alcoholic and knew equally well what would happen to the sobriety of many thousands if he took the road that would lead him *personally* to self-transcendence and God-consciousness (as Princess had put it).

He could not even contemplate such a development. He would deny himself the prospect of divine knowledge if it meant, as he knew it *would* mean, the return of a single AA member to the hell of alcoholism.

He would simply have to continue acting as though the limited life he had chosen for himself was the best life, one that others should emulate.

By remaining ordinary—more perhaps than he really was—he would rescue others.

He would save others by not saving himself.

To save them and to continue to do so, he had to go on thinking as he *had* ... as they did: in short, go on being one of them, recognizably someone they could comfortably relate to.

By this leveling he would protect others. By the revelation of his spiritual ordinariness they would continue to enjoy a peaceful and secure sobriety.

For an indeterminate time he sat at the desk, unaware of how long. It could have been five minutes, or half an hour. He scarcely moved. Outside, the summer night in its stillness and repose mirrored the atmosphere of his mind in the privacy of the studio-retreat. At length he struggled up and decided to make a cup of tea, to stimulate his energies prior to taking his usual walk, if in fact he was going to do so.

As the tea steeped, his mind was still full of the mood of his last reflections and led him to the question he had often asked himself, always wondered about:

If there had been no AA—but if there *had* been a Towns experience—would he still have taken the position to which he had now committed himself? Or was he fooling himself, merely using AA to ultimately repudiate the option of mysticism—the road, its advocates urged upon him, to self-realization ... the path they said would most resolutely oppose the ego and all its works?

He might never know for sure. Because of AA he could never be certain what the answer was. Not for this life, at least.

The only absolute for him was Alcoholics Anonymous.

His journey into the past had made that truth blindingly obvious. It made him a prisoner in a way few men could ever have experienced. But it freed him also—freed him from giving heed to anything else for his life's guidance.

AA was his religion, perhaps the only one he could ever have.

As he drank the tea, seated again at the writing desk, he renewed this idea and focused on the sole problem that need concern him: How to protect AA at all times.

Which in essence also meant: how to protect himself at all times. If he was safe, AA was. If he was not, AA could not be.

He knew his own nature all too well. His aggressive, overbearing egoism, his impulsiveness, willfulness, his false overconfidence, his volatile moodiness: in short, his alcoholic character.

He had to guard himself, his higher self, from *that,* his *other* self; bulwark himself against the possibility of that mutinous core betraying the idealism that was, he knew, his true nature.

Something *extreme* was called for, something inordinate. Some ultimate condition.

A condition that would neutralize his alcoholic propensities day by day, moment by moment.

The condition he in fact had instinctively fallen into once he had fled into the arms of an overweening presence which would prevent him from developing his personality beyond the point it had reached in California but would protect him against himself.

HIS DEPRESSION WAS THE SOLUTION ... to be maintained for as long as necessary, which might be not for five or six years but for the rest of his life ... as Shivani's vision had intimated.

Meditation—and its attendant practices—would have protected him too. He did not have to be told. It would have been the opposite force to the depression—one regenerative, one degenerative. But he could not choose meditation and keep it unknown. It *would* be known.

Just as his special friendship with Chris was known, puzzling more people than Lois about its purpose.

Yes, it would be known and he could not prevent it. Therefore it must not start—and that he could do: prevent it from starting.

Although meditation and its way of life would undoubtedly defend him, in the process of doing so it would be self-defeating, would turn into its opposite. While safeguarding *him* it would challenge, baffle, and even alienate *others*.

They would wonder what had happened to him.

Therefore it must not start and for all his desire—a mixture of curiosity and secret yearning—to enter into its domain, he would not let it.

Depression—that was the answer.

Depression ... without limit, without understanding.

There was no other solution, no other answer. And no escape.

His flight from California was an illusion. Already, even then, the script had been written. He had not been free.

There would be no more flights, no more mirages of escape.

He had passed sentence on himself:

A depression day by day until like a work of God it stretched out into years and decades that was as close to death-in-life, but still some life, as he could discover ... a state wherein he was diverted from the more dangerous aspects of his ego. Paradoxically, the depression was a less hazardous manifestation of that same ego, but in its control he was safe. Miserable, lost, estranged—but safe.

And if he was safe—from himself, from his impulsiveness, his secretive ways, his heavy-handedness, his headstrong potential—AA was safe.

Over and over he had to keep reminding himself of this one vital truth, until it passed into the most inward passages of his brain.

If he failed AA he would have no life, he would in a very short time be drunk and dead.

He did not think what he was doing was noble or self-sacrificing or altruistic. It was something he had to do—and would do. *He had no choice.*

Through Chris, the Princess and Gerald Heard, and through the one moment of his life—that moment at Towns—when he had *lived,* the deity had given him a glimpse of the true promised land of the spirit, the world of meditative truth, of mystical self-transcendence.

And then had denied him the right to enter it. The Moses parallel.

He could not understand these things. The design was too deep and dark for him. He had no choice except to do what he did to save himself not only from the shocked disillusionment of AA but from the justice of God. The depression was little enough of a life but a paradise compared to what he would suffer if he broke his pact with AA and acted to please himself.

• • •

In his past compulsion to neutralize egocentric drives—fear and anxiety, anger and resentment—his alcoholism had in a sense been a similar weapon long ago ... though playing into the power of that same ego to bring it about. Like the situation facing him now, it had seemed the lesser of two evils: both ego-spawned.

Again the idea that had beguiled him earlier: that of the fortunate fall. Everything purposeful, everything meant to play a role in the divine design.

His mind was a confusion of opposites, a merging of contraries....

On the one hand his depression was a metaphysical act of *denial* of what had happened in Los Angeles and of the peculiar conflict (vis-a-vis AA) into which he had been thrown—the flight itself being the first phase of the denial.

At the same time it was a psychic buffer against a course of action—including the acceptance of what Chris was urging—that would result in harming, even destroying, AA. He could not plunge deeply enough into the depression to prevent that from happening— like a criminal who cries, "Catch me before I kill again ... save me from myself."

He now saw his depression in that light and the very realization would work, as already it had, against throwing it off. Although he had "tried everything" to escape from it, even stronger was his urge to embrace it.

Marooned in its depths, full of weakness and self-reproach, he also felt safe.

While in its grip he would not have the daring to convert to Catholicism, the strength to become a mystic, or the desperation to return to drinking.

Hitherto he had often tried to share the leadership of AA with others—even symbolically. *Now* however—and ever since California— there was no vestige of doubt as to what the truth was ... a truth he had denied, recoiled against, fled from, slowly recognized, accepted, and embraced with an urge to sacrifice himself on the altar of AA welfare that was even stronger than his desire to be free.

Through that sacrifice he might in time gain the *spiritual* freedom Princess had spoken of.

• • •

He rose to his feet without effort, feeling alert and energetic, went out into the evening air and breathed deeply. Rich odors of summer enveloped him. The last train of thought had given him sudden new strength, from which he could conclude—apart from his intuition of its power—that it was a thought of Truth.

You shall know the truth and the truth shall make you free.

Any truth would free you. Not only the supreme truth in itself—whatever it might prove to be—but any particular truth supreme *for you*. That, *also,* would free. As he had been.

He began to walk, his mind seeming in rhythm to his body as some of the insights he had received now returned in a mood in which hope was an active ingredient.

But as he moved, it was the central insight about his fusion with AA and what he was prepared to do to protect the fellowship—to die if necessary—to which his mind gravitated. That truth—never known so vividly before this day—had all at once become the anchor of his life, and his reason for living. Clinging to that, as he was now certain he would be able to do, he could endure any ordeal whatever.

It was to arrive at this truth and *to unite his mind to it* that he had taken his journey into the past ... with its realizations. He saw this with such a brilliant flash of awareness that he stopped abruptly on the silent country road and breathlessly listened to the beating of his own thoughts.

The fragrant night in its moonlit repose and overarching benediction seemed to listen also.

Only an hour ago he had been wondering whether it was worthwhile to have made the journey. *It had been.* The vital, life-changing truth he had discovered, or *re*-discovered, had transformed his understanding of everything now and henceforth. Every aspect of consciousness had in a moment been altered.

Such as his desire to be free of the depression ... his knowledge that each year in the past six had been a little less onerous than the previous one, so that even if he continued to do no more than he had he might expect in time to see it gradually recede and fade.

He would cease trying to end or lighten the depression, would make no serious attempt any further to banish it even if he could. He would do nothing to make it worse but just as surely would not terminate it either, even if that were possible. He would live as he could—enduring, waiting, hoping, wanting nothing to be changed, nothing to be different. When it permitted, he would work; when it did not, he would not.

His depression, he knew now, was God-given. Long ago he had been turned into an alcoholic to bring about the creation of AA and for half a decade saddled with a seemingly endless depression to *save* what he created.

He found himself pacing forward along the narrow asphalt road with a strange and buoyant eagerness, as though about to meet something he had passionately anticipated, as though a goal he had long been reaching for was just around the next bend in the road.

To Towns and Akron had to be added the profundity and mystery of this day!

In the consciousness of the great truth that had come to him his heart sang. He felt as he had the evening he had strode back to East Dorset after the long holiday with Lois at Emerald Lake. Now, as then, he seemed possessed by a mystical, providential power bringing him to enlightenment and self-knowledge.

Now he could pray again, could end his fear of closeness to the divine.

He felt young.

Get hold of the deepest truth you can discover, he cried to the listening, moonstill darkness. Make it the center of your life, the touchstone by which all other ideas are judged. Cling to it, worship it, live for it, be prepared to die for it—and you will find happiness, freedom, significance!

AA newcomers invariably wanted to talk about their many problems but he always told them they had only one problem, their drinking, and only one goal, their sobriety. If they made sobriety the center of their universe everything else would come round to it. For *them* sobriety was their highest truth.

For him *now* the truth about the role of AA and the truth about the depression in his life had become the equivalent of sobriety to the individual member—the center of his universe, the standard-truth by which all others would be evaluated. As long as he clung to it and made himself a servant *to* it, its power—its *reality*—would bring him where he wanted to go by means he could not fathom, shield him against influences he could not manage without it, and fulfill him in ways he never could achieve on his own.

Yes, he could pray again. If the depression was God-sent—encompassing him to secure AA, just as his alcoholism had led to both—yes, he could pray!

And if out of the depression could come the insights, power, and joy that were his at this moment, then he would thrive in it as in his own element.

He felt increasingly expansive, magnanimous, transcending his weaknesses....

Perhaps somewhere in the future AA would change, as all things did, and a more complex membership than the one he had known—less damaged by alcohol, less fearful of religion—would be more open to new ideas than those of his time, more demanding that the spiritual challenge posed by such as Chris be embodied in the literature and at the meetings more conspicuously than under his hand.

"Sobriety was not salvation, only a respite. Sobriety experienced for its own sake was an illusion."

Chris' words, etched in his memory. All true.

Not true enough to be accepted and acted upon by himself at *this* point in time. But in ten or twenty years, certainly by the end of the century and long after he and his works were history, AA would change. There would be more like Chris in the fellowship then, more women, more young people, more sensitive souls, more potential mystics, a *flowering* of new types. All of these together with a few far-sighted leaders like Chris might lead AA to the fulfillment of its true purpose, which could not be sobriety alone—sobriety only the foundation, the opening of the door—rather, *spirituality:* self-realization, God-consciousness.

The life Beyond Sobriety.

Long after this age he could see it happening: AA returning to its roots, to its Master and rightful Owner.

AA belonged to the divine being.

It had nothing to do with himself really.

Even from the earliest days in East Dorset he had been a mere instrument in the Lord's hands and AA itself was the Lord's doing from beginning to end. Responsibility was still his to act in the only way he could act now—of *that* there remained not the slightest doubt. But that too was the divine doing and willing ... and planning.

Yes, he could pray now. And would. He already was. The mood that had taken possession of him was itself a prayer.

He saw the lights of an approaching car. It was Lois returning from the train station. With their eyes locked, she sounded the horn softly and waved as she passed. Caught in the glare of the headlights, he waved back, his gesture animated, imbued with energy and optimism. The motion of a man happy to be alive, content to be himself.

What, he asked himself suddenly, standing in the silence that followed the departing car—what was *her* highest truth?

The stillness of the summer night gave the answer.

He was.

Loyalty to *him,* devotion to *him,* faith in *him*—that was her center of gravity, and had been for more than thirty years.

A feeling of awe swept over him.

On an instant he decided to return to the house. It would take him ten or fifteen minutes. She would have much to talk about, would be filled with ideas about the new organization she had called into being, her own version of AA. Tonight of all nights he wanted communication with her, wanted to hear her news, wanted to share with her the new self that had manifested this day. So often in the past she had found him listless and withdrawn but now he would show her the other side of the man in whom she had placed so much hope for so long and for whom she had lived with such undimming faith.

He strode quickly, vigorously forward.

———————————

The Twelve Steps of Alcoholics Anonymous

1. We admitted we were powerless over alcohol—that our lives had become unmanageable.

2. Came to believe that a Power greater than ourselves could restore us to sanity.

3. Made a decision to turn our will and our lives over to the care of God as we understood Him.

4. Made a searching and fearless moral inventory of ourselves.

5. Admitted to God, to ourselves, and to another human being, the exact nature of our wrongs.

6. Were entirely ready to have God remove all these defects of character.

7. Humbly asked Him to remove our shortcomings.

8. Made a list of all the persons we had harmed, and became willing to make amends to them all.

9. Made direct amends to such people wherever possible, except when to do so would injure them or others.

10. Continued to take personal inventory and when we were wrong promptly admitted it.

11. Sought through prayer and meditation to improve our conscious contact with God as we understood Him, praying only for knowledge of His will for us and the power to carry that out.

12. Having had a spiritual awakening as the result of these steps, we tried to carry this message to alcoholics, and to practice these principles in all our affairs.

The Twelve Traditions of Alcoholics Anonymous

1. Our common welfare should come first; personal recovery depends upon AA unity.
2. For our group purpose there is but one ultimate authority— a loving God as He may express Himself in our group conscience. Our leaders are but trusted servants; they do not govern.
3. The only requirement for AA membership is a desire to stop drinking.
4. Each group should be autonomous, except in matters affecting other groups or AA as a whole.
5. Each group has but one primary purpose—to carry its message to the alcoholic who still suffers.
6. An AA group ought never endorse, finance, or lend the AA name to any related facility or outside enterprise, lest problems of money, property, and prestige divert us from our primary purpose.
7. Every AA group ought to be fully self-supporting, declining outside contributions.
8. Alcoholics Anonymous should remain forever nonprofessional, but our service centers may employ special workers.
9. AA, as such, ought never be organized; but we may create service boards or committees directly responsible to those they serve.
10. Alcoholics Anonymous has no opinion on outside issues; hence the AA name ought never to be drawn into public controversy.
11. Our public relations policy is based on attraction rather than promotion; we need always maintain personal anonymity at the level of press, radio and films.
12. Anonymity is the spiritual foundation of all our traditions, ever reminding us to place principles before personalities.

Bibliography

Dr. Bob and the Good Oldtimers, A Biography, with Recollections of Early AA in the Midwest. New York: Alcoholics Anonymous World Services, 1980.

James, William. *The Varieties of Religious Experience,* Garden City, New York: Image books, 1978.

Kurtz, Ernest. *AA The Story* (a revised edition of *Not God: A History of Alcoholics Anonymous.*), San Francisco: Harper & Row Publishers, 1988.

The Language of the Heart: Bill W.'s Grapevine Writings. New York: The AA Grapevine, Inc., 1988.

"Pass It On," The Story of Bill Wilson and How the AA Message Reached the World. New York: Alcoholics Anonymous World Services, 1984.

Thomsen, Robert. *Bill W.* New York: Harper & Row, 1975.

Wilson, Lois B. *Lois Remembers.* New York: The Al-Anon Family Group Headquarters, 1979.

Wilson, William G. *Alcoholics Anonymous Comes of Age.* New York: Alcoholics Anonymous World Services, 1957.

Wilson, William G. *Alcoholics Anonymous.* New York: Alcoholics Anonymous World Services, 1960.

Wilson, William G. *The Twelve Steps and Twelve Traditions.* New York: Alcoholics Anonymous World Services, 1953.

About the Author

PAUL HOURIHAN, teacher and mystic, was born, raised, and educated in Boston where he earned a doctorate in English literature. For 15 years he taught dozens of courses and gave innumerable lectures on the subjects of great mystics and mysticism in Ontario, Canada. For over 45 years he was committed to the spiritual path and a close student of the world's spiritual traditions, particularly India's Vedanta philosophy, and the teachings of her greatest seers.

In the closing period of his life he began, at long last, to publish his compelling works. This is the third of a dozen books on varying subjects, but all with underlying spiritual themes.

He lived with his wife in Northern California, where she continues to carry on his work.

VEDANTIC SHORES PRESS is dedicated to publishing the spiritual works of Paul Hourihan. It was created to help readers reach new shores of spiritual consciousness.

Our creative biographies, novels and non-fiction books, which incorporate Dr. Hourihan's insights from many years of meditative practice, give a clear vision and practical understanding of spirituality and mysticism based on the ancient Indian philosophy of Vedanta.

We are interested in our readers views. If you'd like to comment on *Bill W., A Strange Salvation* or would like more information on our books and audio products, please contact us at:

Vedantic Shores Press
P.O. Box 493100, Redding, CA 96049
Tel: (530) 549-4757   Fax: (530) 549-5743
Toll-free: (866) 549-4757 (U.S. only)
E-mail: info@vedanticshorespress.com

OR visit our website at
www.VedanticShoresPress.com